LASERS ACROSS THE CHERRY ORCHARD

By Dr. Michael Forrest

Peacock, Wilkock and Forrest, and Derek Robinson

МосКВА

The Author

Michael Forrest was born in London but grew up in Aberdare, South Wales and was educated in Jones's West Monmouthshire Grammar School, Pontypool. He was a first generation Sandwich Course student in Glamorgan Technical College (now the University of Glamorgan) and studied Applied Physics. Graduating in 1957 he joined the United Kingdom Atomic Energy Authority at Harwell and later Culham Laboratory (Oxfordshire) to work on the then top secret project on Controlled Nuclear Fusion.

He played a pivotal role in the development of Laser Light Scattering as the standard method of measuring the temperatures of 10- to 100,000,000 degrees Celsius, the operating temperatures required for Fusion Reactors.

As a result, Russian researchers invited him and a U.K.A.E.A. team to Moscow to confirm their controversial Tokamak experimental results. This was to lead to collaborative experiments in Frascati (Rome), Lisbon, Tripoli and Dusseldorf, and invited talks in Stockholm, Princeton (U.S.A.) and Japan.

He is a Ph.D. examiner for the Universities of London, Glasgow, Sydney and Dublin. Publications include 43 refereed journal papers and over 100 conference papers. For his pioneering research work he was awarded a Higher Doctorate. He is a Chartered Physicist and is a Fellow of the Institute of Physics. Currently his life story and career is being recorded for the British Library project *An Oral History of British Science.*

LASERS ACROSS THE CHERRY ORCHARDS

By

Michael Forrest
D. Sc., C. Phys., F. Inst. P.

'A fantastic symbol of experimental skill, international collaboration and truly the starting point of international Fusion research.'

Prof. Manfred von Hellerman

'Your book about international collaboration with the Russians on Nuclear Fusion is of great interest and I hope it attracts a wide readership. As Minister of Technology I signed various technological agreements with the U.S.S.R and I hope it helped improve our relations.'

Tony Benn

LUCE SCIENTIÆ VINCES

Printed and bound in the U.K. by Tandem Press
www.tandempress.com

Acknowledgements

Over a career spanning five decades any of my scientific achievements have been due to collaborations and friendships with numerous physicists, engineers, technicians and administrators.

My closest associates have been Professor Patrick Carolan, Peter Wilcock, Dr. Phil. Morgan, Dr. Michael Walsh, Harry Jones, Martin Dunstan, Dr. David Muir, Professor Manfred Von Hellerman, Professor K. Muroaka, Dr. Glen Counsel, Dr Kieran Gibson and Brian Boland. I was introduced into the complex world of Plasma Physics by Dr. Peter McWhirter and Dr Alan Gibson who both kindled my interest in the development of plasma diagnostic techniques.

Sadly, several of the most inspiring scientists I had the pleasure of working with are no longer with us: Professor Nicol Peacock my exciting and stimulating leader over many years; Dr David Evans, who greatly broadened my knowledge of physics and the arts; Dr. Derek Robinson F.R.S., impressively a theoretician and experimentalist of the highest order; Professor Dan Bradley F.R.S. (Imperial College), who brought optics to life for me; Professor Sir Robert (Bob) Wilson F.R.S., whose farsightedness led to my career in the development of laser diagnostics. I was privileged to enjoy both the friendship and professional guidance of Dr. John Lawson F.R.S., a legendary figure in plasma physics and particle accelerators. Dr R. (Bas) S. Pease F.R.S. gave us pioneers of Laser Light Scattering diagnostics his unqualified support. For many years he strongly urged me to write this account of our work.

My thanks also go to Professor Bryan Taylor F.R.S. for his account of how, as a weapons scientist, he first became involved with Fusion Energy research and for his encouragement in the production of this book.

Our success in Moscow was due to the unstinting help of Dr Slava Strelkov, the Tokamak group leader and pioneer, Dr Dennis Ivanov, Dr. John Sheglov, Dr Asa Razamova, Dr.Volodiya Sannikov, our closest collaborator, and the Russian technicians. The British team owes much to Mrs Marion Robinson who helped hold the British team together in body and soul while in Moscow.

My personal friend Ron Turnbull, previously of the Oxford Newspaper Group, has given me useful editorial advice. I have received considerable encouragement and support from the Culham Centre for Fusion Energy, in particular Nick Holloway, Jennifer Hay, Chris Warwick, Dr Martin O'Brien and Stuart Morris.

Of course, through all my scientific adventures I have always enjoyed the support of my wife Annita and all of our family.

The front cover design is based on an original water colour by my grand-daughter Sophie Arquimbau.

The photograph on the back cover was taken during a break in a cross country skiing expedition. Slava Stelkov, the Tokamak group leader, has the red hat and the author a red jacket. Photograph courtesy of the Kurchatov Institute, Moscow.

Preface

The panacea for the Worlds future prime energy base – Nuclear Fusion.

Nuclear Fusion is the fundamental energy source of the universe; it is the process that powers our sun. In the laboratory, scientists have striven to emulate this natural reactor by fusing together deuterium ('heavy' hydrogen) and tritium ('super heavy' hydrogen). The sun requires a temperature of about 15 million degrees Celsius to create this reaction because of its massive gravitational forces that heat and compress the fusion fuel. In comparison the earth's gravity is very weak and researchers create the optimum conditions by heating a low density plasma to much higher temperatures of 100 million degrees Celsius. Magnetic fields are then used to confine and control this nuclear furnace for the benefit of man.

The creation of a practical Fusion Reactor has proved to be an ongoing and formidable challenge to Nuclear Scientists. This is the story of the author's role in the major scientific breakthroughs that have led to the dream of a Fusion powered world becoming a reality in the foreseeable future.

Lasers Across the Cherry Orchards

By Dr. Michael Forrest

Chapter 1

1969 was a thrilling year, a confident year for mankind. Man walked on the moon, Concorde made its maiden flight, a generation wallowed in the mud at Woodstock. But this year was also to provide the focus for a unique true story behind dramatic cutting edge scientific research at the height of the 'Cold War' and my involvement as a young physicist.

I was to be privileged to join nuclear scientists from the major Western and Eastern bloc countries in a great scientific adventure. Many of these scientists had been associated with their national nuclear weapon programmes but now they had dramatically switched from nuclear bomb makers to 'star' makers.

They had become fascinated by the challenge to exploit Nuclear Fusion as the future prime energy source for the world. This would be the ultimate solution to two of the most serious problems facing the modern world, those of global warming and the fast diminishing world oil reserves.

Nuclear Fusion is the process that powers the sun and is also utilised to make the hydrogen bomb. Imagine if we could build a reactor on Earth that mimics this awesome energy source in a controlled fashion. To do this we need to fuse two special types of hydrogen fuel together which requires temperatures of 100,000,000 degrees Celsius and then to contain the resulting plasma to sustain the reaction.

This interest in nuclear fusion had its origins in the United Kingdom, the United States and the Soviet Union. All the work was carried out in the utmost secrecy. This was because any potential neutron source was considered to be of great military significance, a major consideration in those days of the tense nuclear war stand-off between the NATO and Warsaw Pact countries.

One of the most intriguing aspects of this remarkable transition of interests was triggered by an amazing train of events back in 1950. A young Red Army Sergeant Oleg Lavrentiev was serving out his 'national service' on the remote and bleak Soviet island of Sakhalin in the Barents sea. He had not then had the advantage of a university education but he was to have a major effect on Soviet and ultimately world nuclear science.

He wrote a letter to Academician A. D. Sakharov, the leading Soviet Physicist and Nuclear Weapons scientist, with ideas on how to create a hydrogen bomb. More interestingly, in the same letter he also suggested how an arrangement of grids surrounding an electrically heated hydrogen gas could be the basis for a fusion reactor. Instead of dismissing these ideas out of hand the great man gave the fusion reactor idea his careful consideration and within a few months Sakharov stimulated by this young soldier's letter came up with his own ideas. This was: to use magnetic fields to provide a cage for these high temperature plasmas or ionised gas.

Nature has its own solution to the problem, the sun's huge mass provides enough gravitational force to contain its sustainable fusion reactor on which planet earth depends for all human existence.

Working with I. E. Tamm, the leading Soviet Nuclear Weapons expert, Sakharov completed the first evaluation of a Magnetic Thermonuclear Reactor, as they called it. This concept was enthusiastically taken up by the leading nuclear scientists, notably Academician I. V. Kurchatov, and after a workshop attended by designers of atomic weapons, proposals for a MTR were put to the Minister of the Electric Industry. Progress was stalled by the institutionalised bureaucracy of the Communist party that held sway on all decision making at the time in that dystopian country, much to the dismay of the scientists.

Then there was sensational news from the most unlikely of sources – President Juan Peron of Argentina. He announced to the world at large that 'a German scientist, Ronald Richter, had succeeded in the controlled release of atomic energy at super high temperatures of millions of degrees Celsius without using uranium fuel'. This apparently had taken place in a specially created secret laboratory on the Hewmall Island belonging to Argentina.

Minister Efremov on hearing this startling news burst into the Chief Goverment Scientist Kurchatov's study without any ceremony. We do not know what conversation ensued, but with praiseworthy alacrity the top Russian Scientific establishment was galvanised into action. The bullish Academician Lev Artsimovitch was taken off his weapon orientated Isotope Separation work to head up the new experimental Fusion program and Academician M. A. Leontovitch was chosen by Tamm to lead the Theoretical side.

The priority now given to the project can be gauged by the fact that the USSR Council of Ministers ordered key Industrial Plants to support the new fusion project. This had been pre-authorised by Joseph Stalin in May 1951. The most talented University Ph.D. graduates were now directed to controlled thermonuclear research rather than to the weapons establishments. The communist system strongly believed in the direction of labour in all fields of endeavour, especially for prestige projects.

After many false starts in the following five years the most promising route proved to be a toroidal or doughnut shaped device known as the *Tokamak*. In this vessel the high temperature hydrogen plasma was confined and heated in what was in effect the secondary of a huge transformer. An extra set of coils was added to provide a magnetic field that combined with that from the electric current in the plasma. The resulting magnetic cage proved to be the secret for the confinement of high temperature plasmas.

Rarely can the saying 'great minds think alike' be such a truism. However, in the case of Nuclear Fusion this happened with great effect: Russian, American and British working independently came up with the essentially concept.

In 1946, a young Australian Peter Thoneman and his colleagues were working under the direction of Professor Lindeman in the Clarendon Laboratory, beautifully situated on the edge of the University Parks in Oxford. They experimented with plasmas in glass toroids surrounded by copper coils to stabilise the so-called kinks in the plasma. This coincided with the work of G. P. Thomson and Moses Blackman at Imperial College, London, who obtained a classified patent for a toroidal nuclear fusion reactor using deuterium, a type of hydrogen. It was to be 1948 before Alan Ware was to start experimental work in the University and within three years the project was moved to Associated Electrical Industries in Aldermaston for security reasons.

Meanwhile, across the Atlantic in the United States, Teller, Tuck and Ulam held closed seminars on the various new ideas. Here, as with the Russians, there was a tortuous procession of various plasma devices leading up to a toroidal device, the *Stellerator.*

Then in 1958 the world was subjected to yet another dramatic announcement, this carried considerably more gravitas than the Argentinean claims some seven years earlier. The highly respected British journal Nature reported results from the Harwell based *ZETA* experiment claiming temperatures of tens of millions of degrees Celsius and neutrons of thermonuclear origin. The press and TV gave the story immense coverage with headlines promising 'unlimited power from seawater' etc. and Harwell scientists were given the glamour treatment and accorded film star status, much to their intense embarrassment.

This optimism proved to be premature, basically due to the lack of understanding of the 'detail of the underlying physics' at that time. Ironically *ZETA* was very similar to the Russian *Tokamak* in many ways, but critically there was a failure to arrange the two main magnetic fields in what is now believed to be the optimum way.

Chapter 2

ZETA was to provide the starting point of my scientific career, in 1957. This was as the result of one of life's random throws of the dice that determines man's destiny. In the final year of my Applied Physics course, the head of the physics department had asked an old friend of his from Harwell to give final year students a talk on 'Electronics in Research at Harwell'. He was Eric Pulsford who had made important contributions to electronic warfare developments in the Malvern Research Establishment during the Second World War.

Impressed by his lecture, my friend Albert Packwood and I approached him afterwards and asked him how we could set about trying for a job in Harwell – then a closed world as far as we were concerned. 'No problem', he said. 'I will send you application forms when I get back to Harwell tomorrow'. As good as his word, a set of application forms arrived a few days later. This was followed up by an invitation to attend an interview at Harwell in the General Physics Division, Hangar 7.

It was with some trepidation that I travelled up from my home town, Aberdare, again regarded as the most attractive of the Welsh mining valleys, restored to its former green splendour after having recovered from the industrial revolution.

I recount the journey in some detail because it represents a cameo of that period before the 1960's when life became a lot less leisurely. To this day I can remember the train journey from Cardiff headed by the steam engine Trenaton Castle, whose name registered with me instantly because, like almost every school boy in those days, I had in my younger days been an avid collector of railway engine numbers, which would be ticked off in the famous Allen series of books which listed every engine number. I suppose the modern equivalent would be the computer nerd or games addict. Nearing my destination, the Cardiff to Paddington main line passed through the Vale of the White Horse and then through Swindon, the centre of the Great Western Railway, with rows of giant steam engines lined up outside the giant engine sheds. They were awaiting the glamorous 'Header' name-plates to be fitted – and what powerful emotions they would evoke: The Cornish Riviera Express, The Royal Duchy, The Red Dragon, The Bristolian, and The Devonian. What images these names conjured up as these engineering thoroughbreds thundered through Brunel's network of iron roads to all points Westwards from London. I was in the Didcot 'slip' coach which was cast off from the main body of the train while the train was travelling at its maximum speed. This clever idea enabled the express to cut out one stop without any consequential loss of time to its schedule. The guard skilfully bringing it to a smooth halt at a pre-determined point on the platform. Such a procedure would give the health and safety eunuchs of today a heart attack. In those days Didcot was not the most impressive of towns to arrive in, in fact I found it quite depressing, and wondered what I had let myself in for.

The last stage was on a local bus. I was the only passenger and the driver was keen to give me a running commentary as we wended our way through the Berkshire countryside. The road went through Harwell village and past the old *Crispin* pub, and was lined with red brick, white wattled half-timbered and thatched cottages, inter-spaced with some elegant period houses. Turning left at the Rowstock crossroads, the driver explained with some relish that according to local legend it was haunted by a midnight stage-coach and four. Then we were driving along, flanked on both sides by the famous Harwell cherry orchards.

After a short climb, the bus breasted the hill and the gentle descent was as if the steep sides of the valleys that I had been brought up in had been folded back and the world had literally opened up for me.

This was the world of the so called 'barley millionaire farmers' and the horse-racing fraternity whose peace had been so rudely disturbed in 1939 by the building of an airfield to house the World War Two airmen and their Wellington bombers. The flyers were then, in turn, replaced in 1946 by the Atomics who commandeered the airfield to site the United Kingdom Atomic Energy Authority Research Establishment.

I was a couple of hours too early for my interview and as I left the bus the driver suggested I should go for lunch at the *Horse and Jockey*, about half a mile past the Harwell main gates Hardly a pub, I was there faced by the most lavish buffet I had seen in my life. The landlord, a tweed clad ex-army officer type, welcoming but intimidating at the same time, took me in at a glance. 'You must be on the way to Harwell,' he said. I explained myself and I told him that I was very impressed by his table. I suppose I must have had the impoverished student look about me and had said the right thing about the food. 'Take a plate and help yourself to whatever you like for five bob and have your first Berkshire Ale on the house.' He explained at some length that most of his customers were gentlemen farmers, racehorse trainers, jockeys, or owners, plus gentlefolk from villages like Blewbury and Upton. Rather significantly he did not mention scientists. It struck me that there was obviously a pecking order in this part of the world and I wondered how and if I was going to fit in.

Fortified by the excellent food and nerves calmed by a couple of drinks, I walked to the Harwell main entrance. Behind the high security fence I could see huge aircraft hangars and strange looking chimneys and towers. Passing through the security gates I was intercepted by the friendly but armed U.K.A.E.A. police. They directed me to a lady receptionist who badged me and asked me to sign an official secrets document. A guard escorted me to the huge brick wartime hangar H7, only a short walk from the main gate. A small door was let into a giant grey steel roller door. Inside was another layer of security, the photoplaque system, this is where you cannot enter unless your photo is there on a display board.

Inside, the noise and smell of big science hit me for the first time. A background noise of humming electrical machinery and hissing hydraulics, the bleeping of radiation monitors, the audible countdown to firing experimental shots. Then there was the combined smell of hot oil, ozone, solvents and of selenium, used in rectifiers in those days.

The hangar was very efficiently arranged, three floors of galleries lining the inside walls, which housed offices and small labs, plus a couple of meeting rooms, while the experimental equipment occupied the extensive central floor area, separated by further security barriers. The concrete floor was sealed by a shiny grey paint which appeared to be almost clinically clean. There were large numbers of grey vacuum dewars on stands emitting clouds of what I later learned was liquid nitrogen vapour used in vacuum pumps which were common to practically every piece of plasma physics equipment.

Then I was ushered into an interview room for the first of several nerve jangling boards that I was to be subjected to in my subsequent physics career. The board consisted of the chairman, Geoff. Harding, who was a very senior scientist, flanked by two scientists each side of him, each representing a different Harwell physics discipline, and to complete the panel, a personnel officer who kept records of the interview. The chairman, a charming man, introduced himself and the others just by name, so I had no idea what they did or what they represented.

I was asked to describe in three or four minutes what relevant experience and interests I had outside the physics course I had just completed. I was fortunate in having plenty of interests to talk about, as I was the first generation of the new type Sandwich Student. This was a pioneering scheme based on students taking a four years course during which alternatively, six months was spent in College and six months in industry.

I explained to them that the most interesting and exciting were the two sessions in the Rolls Royce Aero Division, Derby, working on the *Conway*, the first by-pass jet engine. My task was to survey the temperatures inside the combustion chambers, to check that no hot spots occurred. I explained that this was of critical importance as any localised overheating could be fatal to the engine.

What I did not tell them about was the most memorable event that happened during that time, as it would have been out of context in the interview.

Late one evening I was with two of the elite engine testers, who were entrusted to run the most advanced projects – in this case the first 100-hour run of this unique jet engine. With a few hours to go of what had been an uneventful test, these two old Rolls Royce hands decided to go for a 'smoke' leaving me in charge for a few minutes with a crib list of when and how to shut the engine down in case of any trouble.

After about half an hour, I was startled by the entrance of two men. The taller and older of the two was ruddy faced and in a tweed suit. The other, slighter, had a military appearance and was somehow familiar. In a booming friendly voice with a distinct Derbyshire accent, he said, 'I am Hives, the Chairman. More importantly, this is Frank Whittle', he added with a smile, 'who you will have heard of. He is very interested in the Conway and its technical aspects.' His smile faded when on looking around he realized I was on my own in charge of Rolls Royce's most important project

I gave them a quick run down on my project and before I could start on the daunting task of explaining the principles of the bypass jet engine to the inventor of the original Jet engine the testers strolled in, their faces paling in horror as they realised they were in trouble.

Very quietly Hives looked at these two veterans and said, 'Good evening gentlemen, this young chap here has been giving us a very competent progress report on the 100-hour test, perhaps you would like to add your half-pennys worth'. But of course I had not even begun to explain what was going on. Lord Hives and Whittle were quizzing me on the efficiency of the Sandwich course and how it worked out in practice.

Later, over a 'mash', the local Derbyshire expression for a cup of tea, I plucked up courage to ask Lord Hives how he started in Rolls Royce. Looking slightly startled at my question, he replied: 'I was Royce's first apprentice'. Frank Whittle registered my surprise and how impressed I was and said: 'There is some thing for you to tell your grandchildren.'

But it hardly goes without saying I had two exciting things to tell future generations. This was to be my first encounter with really famous men in a career that was to lead to further privileged contacts.

Then a less exotic, but still interesting experience, was with the Central Electricity Authority commissioning new power stations which involved testing the efficiency of the huge Babcock boilers and other newly installed equipment. My enthusiasm was somewhat diminished when I found myself on my 21st birthday a few hundred feet up on the outside of a smoke stack in Carmarthen Bay Power Station, testing the efficiency of the electrostatic precipitators.

The interview panel all seemed very interested in these practical experiences and also of my hobby of photography and subjected me to questions on the detailed optics involved and what technical skills I had mastered. I had expected a real gruelling on scientific topics, but to my immense relief, they had only left time for a couple of token physics questions.

I was sent out for fifteen minutes, to kick my heels, and then called back in to hear my fate. The chairman said: 'Congratulations. Unofficially, you will be receiving a job offer, subject to your security clearance'. He turner to Peter McWhirter who was to be my future boss: 'Perhaps you could explain to young Forrest what we have decided'.

This very courteous Scotsman smiled and said: 'I think with your background you would fit in best with my group. BUT, I can't tell you what the post involves because it is classified. What I can tell you, though, is that you will enjoy it. I don't know how you feel about that'. The other board members nodded as if encouraging me to say 'yes'. The rest, as they say, is history.

They could not even show me around until I had received the appropriate security clearance. Afterwards, on the train journey back to Wales, it was with a sense of excited anticipation that I pondered what this interesting job would be.

I was staying at my future wife's house in Aberdare when the security officer came to interview me. He explained that he was seconded from Naval Intelligence to help clear the backlog caused by the rapid expansion of the United Kingdom

Atomic Authority. A jovial, disarming chap, he laughed and said: 'You staying with your girl friend has cleared one hurdle'. He explained that homosexuals were a serious security risk as they were very vulnerable to blackmail, as such practices were illegal then. Nowadays it seems that security checks are more concerned with ones financial probity.

There was also a strong element of comedy, because I had given my doctor, Jack Wilson, as a reference. Driving along and lost in this long winding Welsh valley, the security officer stopped to ask a lady in the street where he could find Dr Wilson. He was directed to a surgery and introduced himself to this affable doctor. After his standard preamble, he was interrupted: 'I think you have the wrong Dr Wilson young man, I am Alistair. Jack is my twin brother. Also for good measure, I am a founder member of the local Communist Party'. They both enjoyed a good laugh about it.

On recounting the story to me he said, 'wait until I tell them about this back in Whitehall I will never live it down, but I must admit Dr Alistair was the most charming man'.

Chapter 3

My security clearance went through with no further ado, but then I had to make a further trip to Harwell for a very vigorous medical, which all radiation workers are subjected to. In fact I don't think there is another area of work where the health of employees is so carefully monitored.

A month later I reported for duty at Harwell. First, I was told at the main gate: 'you must go and see Amy Croker, the most important person on site'. This legendary lady in Building 77, which housed the Directorate, was the human focal point of this gigantic establishment. She issued your first temporary pass and set in train the process for your permanent photoplaque version and your various radiation monitoring badges. A chain-smoking, unmarried, very genteel lady, you were instantly her friend and she would take an intense interest in every aspect of your life in the nicest possible way. What is more, she treated everybody from the Director to casual labourers the same. As somebody once said: 'we were her family'.

Then my research career was to start in earnest. Peter McWhirter was now free to explain what was going on behind this massive security blanket. He described what controlled thermonuclear fusion was about. To me the concept was mind-blowing and most of the physics terminology was new to me, which was pretty un-nerving. He then took me into the *ZETA* control room, where I was confronted with a large control desk with three white-coated scientists seated in front of it. In the centre were a couple of circular cathode ray tubes with their luminous green glow. These were the original TV type tubes that monitored the electrical signals from the various measuring devices. The rest of the panels were filled with electrical meters and vacuum and pressure gauges and knobs to adjust the high voltages and currents used. The back wall was lined with racks of grey paneled electronic units. Then I was shown a suite of laboratories packed with measuring equipment, most of which I had never seen before, one of which was to become my territory, the spectroscopy lab. This is where the light emitted from the *ZETA* plasma was directed to an array of instruments for analysis. These custom-built rooms surrounded *ZETA*, housed in its massive concrete bunker.

ZETA itself was an impressive piece of electrical and mechanical engineering, it was essentially a huge transformer with a three-metre diameter hollow aluminium doughnut threaded through it. Inside this, was a stainless steel bellows liner. The plasma was generated by inducing a current of 200,000 amps in the hydrogen gas contained in the torus. The overall impression was a complex web of thick black electrical cables and massive polished stainless steel vacuum pumps cloaked in clouds of liquid nitrogen vapour.

I found myself cast into the real world of physics research at the sharp end. I was not too surprised to find the top layer of scientists were almost exclusively from Oxford and Cambridge Universities, mostly with backgrounds in war-time military research. However the younger middle grade scientists and the younger recruits were from a much wider spread of universities, including the so-called red brick universities.

One of the first things that struck me was that that I was suddenly immersed in the scientific equivalent of the 'Tower of Babel'. A completely new vocabulary had to be mastered.

Then there was the sophisticated array of spectrometers, Hilger Glass, Hilger Quartz, Three Metre Ebert, and Fabry Perots. Even one of the simplest electrical devices, a coil to measure electrical current, rejoiced in the non-descriptive name of a Rogowski.

More challenging was the specialised terminology of plasma physics itself, all of which hinges on the behaviour of charged particles in a magnetic field: Diamagnetism, Bremsstrahlung, Langmuir Oscillations, Landau damping, Fokker Planck diffusion coefficients, and Rayleigh Taylor instabilities, were some examples.

I soon learned not to be shy about asking about terminology or in fact any physics I had not come across before. In those days a lot of the things we dealt with were not yet in the standard textbooks. However, there was no excuse for ignorance as I was surrounded by a breathtaking array of academic and practical experts all willing to help a learner plasma physicist.

On most days, Ted Butt, the grandly titled Chief Experimental Officer would be in the control seat setting up the machine conditions and directing the whole operation. A bluff, loud, genial man, used to being in command, but with a boundless enthusiasm which was infectious. A team of vacuum, electronic and mechanical technicians were dancing attendance to his every direction: 'Change this', 'check that', 'can we have more volts on the main bank', 'there is too much noise on the probe signal'. His commands and observations were barked out. It was as if he was conducting an orchestra. He was, in fact, orchestrating a complex experiment to optimise its performance.

Young white-coated scientific assistants stood around waiting to develop the films that recorded every electrical signal. Impatient to see the result of each shot, Ted would grab the dripping wet 35 mm films to get a glimpse of the results of the plasma shot. Lesser mortals would have been reprimanded for spoiling the film. Rows of cameras, derived from wartime military versions, recorded every signal, which were then analysed by the scientific staff according to their interest. There were no computers in those days it was all hand calculations with slide rules and even log tables.

I was startled to discover there was even a dedicated mathematician by the name of Whipple in support to help the less theoretical scientists, or experimentalists, solve the more complex equations that went along with plasma physics. The poor chap's world fell apart when his only son was killed in a mountaineering accident on Snowdon. Exactly a year later his body was found on Snowdon in the same spot. Sadly, that was not the end of the Snowdon mountain tragedies. A few years later we were to lose another colleague and his new bride who died together when an ice cornice collapsed under them.

The lead physicist was R. S. (Bas) Pease an ebullient pipe smoking Cambridge man of impeccable breeding. He was a descendant of Edward R. Pease, a founder of the socialist Fabian movement. He had been a young officer in the RAF in the new field of Operational Research, as applied to Intelligence analysis. He exuded confidence and enjoyed a combatant style of discussion, developed from a blooding in the university debating societies and an intellectual family that was related to the Huxleys and Wedgewoods. He lived in a large rambling ex-brewer's house in the Horse Racing village of West Ilsey, just a few miles over the Downs from the site, which boasted a huge music room. A few miles further on in another village, Uffington, was John Betjeman's house, or rather his wife's and children's, because he spent most of his time in London on his many literary projects and other activities.

I was to be a plasma atomic spectroscopist. For the uninitiated, this is someone who studies the light emitted from the plasmas used in the fusion process and tries to interpret and determine the temperatures and behaviour of the very hot gases. The light is split into its constituent colours, or spectral lines, by passing it through a prism or reflecting it off a diffraction grating, a mirror with a thousand grooves per inch cut in it. It is then detected either on photographic plates or by photomultipliers.

My first task was to design an instrument that could do this very efficiently and with great precision, known generally as a spectrometer. The existing ones were unstable and frankly not up to the job. Even to this day such an instrument forms the key part of the optical systems used to measure the 100,000,000-degree Celsius temperatures necessary for a fusion reactor.

I hit on the idea of mounting all the optical components on a cylindrical body giving it great stability and managed to improve the optics to channel more light through the instrument. These became known, somewhat unkindly, by my colleagues, as 'Mikes sewer pipes', because these were actually used to make the prototype instruments. These instruments became the work-horses for spectroscopic measurements and one would be crucial to our later success in Russia.

In no time at all I was immersed in the *ZETA* experimental work, struggling to record the spectral lines emitted from the plasma on photographic plates, so we could see how hot and dense the plasma was. We sometimes worked through the night to get strong enough images recorded on what was, by today's standards, a very insensitive medium. We tried every trick in the book to make the emulsion on the plates more sensitive to the light we were analysing: from pre-sensitising with a flash of light to stewing the plates in hot developer.

Harwell's distinguished and inspirational Director, Sir John Cockroft O.M., lived on the site in what had been in wartime the RAF Station Commanders house. Some nights he would come to visit those of us who were working late on *ZETA,* via the Social Club bar, and bring in a crate of beer: strictly against the regulations, but nobody would have had the nerve to question him. Actually, I suspect the security guards would have helped him carry the contraband in through the

With great enthusiasm he would question the various leaders in great detail on the experiments carried out during that day. He certainly kept his finger on the pulse of the experiment.

One night he said he was concerned that it took so long to record our data and he sat down beside me in a blacked out optical lab. It was a surrealistic experience with both of us supping beer out of Pyrex glass chemical beakers. He went through the optics with me in great detail to see how we could improve things. Short of major technological advances we decided the optics were optimised and we would just have to carry on. Sir John was very kind and friendly and I found him easy to talk to, and he treated you as if you were at his intellectual level. To this day I still remember this interaction I had with this distinguished Nobel Laureate.

I had only been working on *ZETA* for a few months when the authorities decided to declassify the fusion programme. This was largely because the Russians had sensationally, in the person of Academician Igor Kurchatov, given a talk in Harwell a year earlier describing their work.

These revelations totally shocked the U.K.A.E.A. fusion hierarchy for two reasons. Firstly that the Russians would reveal details of such a sensitive topic and secondly the great advances they had made in plasma physics.

I found myself, as a very junior scientist, involved in the ensuing press release (or melée, as some people described it at the time). My task was to look after a cub TV reporter by the name of Alan Whicker, unknown to me at the time. He struck me at the time as a caricature of a Fleet Street reporter, very dapper with Brylcreemed hair and a light military-style Macintosh. Not being a science correspondent he admitted he was daunted in having to interview Cockcroft for the main BBC Six O'clock TV News without having a clue what fusion was about. Apparently the press briefing by the *ZETA* senior staff had been too technical for him to grasp and he asked if I would give him a layman's version. In our tea-room, I gave him a simplified description of the principles involved, for which he seemed both grateful and relieved. I have seen him on Television countless times since, full of confidence and each time I smile to myself remembering how he started his career.

Step forward 50 years and Alan Gibson and myself are interviewed by Roland Pease – the son of R.S. (Bas) Pease! – a BBC Science Correspondent and Senior Producer. This was broadcasted on 16th January 2008 on BBC Radio 4 in a programme called 'Britain's Sputnik' to celebrate the 50th anniversary of *ZETA*, in which we gave our recollections of the exciting early days of the project.

Chapter 4

Now, instead of an old Welsh mining town, I found myself living in what must be one of the most attractive Thames-side villages, Sutton Courtenay. I was in digs with five other Harwell employees in what was affectionately known as 'Dyer's doss House'. It was really quite well appointed and comfortable despite this somewhat unkind description. A kindly, retired Cockney couple ran the place with a son who would certainly never have passed the Harwell security checks. We drank the local Morland Brewery beers and played bar billiards, a new game to me, in the *Swan* pub. This was situated at the back of the village green and mainly frequented by the locals who took a few weeks to accord us newcomers with a nod and a friendly 'alright?' These days the Swan has moved considerably up market as a gastro-pub where I meet up, monthly, with retired work colleagues to discuss affairs of the moment, rarely of the past. One of the more mature lodgers was an ex-Royal Navy engineer, who worked at Harwell as a reactor operator. He had been invalided out of the Navy with a chest complaint and a generous pension. With this financial buffer he became a semi-professional gambler for a hobby as he had no family or dependants to worry about. Like most of his kind he had a secret system: successful or not we never found out. But he did say he never bet more than his pension and the couple of times he took me racing he seemed to be on first name terms with a lot of the bookies. To be fair he always urged me not to bet. I expect because he knew I was engaged to a girl back in Wales. 'Chapel as well!' as a Welsh native would say.

Close by was the church where author George Orwell (Eric Blair) of *Nineteen Eighty Four* fame is buried. Former Prime Minister Asquith's elegant riverside house was just a few hundred metres away, surprisingly accessible from the main road and the riverside path that leads to the Thames weirs. It still has direct telephone connections to 10, Downing Street, a very proud previous owner confided to my family many years later when we were walking past one Sunday afternoon. Apparently this connection will be severed if ever anybody tries to telephone No. 10, whatever the reason.

At weekends we headed to Abingdon, three miles away, a ancient and touristy Thames riverside town, which I was destined to make my future home. This provided a heady array of pubs complete with the world famous *Morlands* brewery renowned for its *Old Speckled Hen* brew and a somewhat sad cinema. The MG Car Company was still an important employer and strongly associated with Abingdon. Just on the edge of the town, the cars, MG Midgets and MGBs, would trundle off the production line and be taken out by test drivers for a drive around the perimeter of the RAF airfield. I was told by an employee, who lived close to my family home, that if they made it back to the factory: 'they were OK'. He was one of the elite, who prepared the highly successful rally cars in the special tuning department. From the other side of the road he would listen to my 3 litre Austin Westminster saloon ticking over and tell me whether the twin S.U. carburettors on the engine were balanced.

One could enjoy a palpable sense of wickedness in those days on entering *The Nags Head* pub, situated on an island that splits the bridge spanning the Thames on the road leading to Henley. This was a real 'horse racing' pub. All day on Saturdays it was packed with jockeys past and present, trainers, owners, and even bookies and their runners. All these varied characters had come in from the surrounding legendary racing villages of Blewbury, Upton, the Hagbournes, the Hendreds and the Ilseys. This was to me an exotic world. But there was also the criminal fringe element who were there to plan betting coups and nobble the jockeys. An insider told me that a lot of them were based in London and from their sharp dress and accents I could believe this.

In fact, very sadly, this was to affect us in Harwell. Our lavishly stocked stores, where one could obtain almost any item required to build and carry out experiments, were staffed largely by diminutive ex-jockeys who, for some reason I could never fathom, took to this role with great enthusiasm. They were always ready to recount stories of their glory days in the Horse Racing world.

Then suddenly one day we were shocked to read in the National Newspapers that our very own store man had killed himself. Apparently he had become involved with a horse racing syndicate who took advantage of his virtually free access to every racing stable around the area and his ability to get at any racing horse that they wanted to interfere with. He must have got wind of the fact that the specialist police horse racing squad were on to him and he could not face the prospect of a long jail sentence. Or possibly, more chillingly, the underworld may well have him silenced for good.

Back at the work-face, we were wrestling with the immense complexities of the plasma, the extent of which became more apparent to us by the day. We were handicapped in our determination of the plasma temperatures by the limitations of spectroscopy. As a result, it was impossible to say with any great accuracy what all our efforts on *ZETA* were achieving. We were attempting to measure the plasma temperatures of five million degrees Celsius or so with an accuracy of 30% – at best.

Chapter 5

My early years at Harwell were to be interrupted by what was a regular career hazard of that period, namely that of two years of National Service. I was very surprised when I received my call-up papers with orders to report to an infantry regiment: The Queen's Royal Regiment. I had nominated a technical corps or regiment because of my scientific qualifications so this was the last kind of military posting I had expected. Now under military regulations I was not in a position to argue, and on reporting to the Stoughton Barracks in Guildford, I found myself in one of the top fighting regiments, known as *The 2nd Afoot,* or the second most senior infantry regiment in the British army.

This was the Regiment that famously 'stood on the burning deck' and drowned to save the women and children on board. I still have my cap badge (a lamb rampant on symbolic waves). Such is the pride that the army can instil into a reluctant conscript, even after just a few weeks exposure to the military culture.

Then it was ten weeks of traditional square bashing in which we were taught the rudiments of drill, introduced to weapons, and even bayonet fighting. The latter was the most frightening experience in my life, ordered to run at and bayonet a sergeant, a grizzled veteran of the Korean War, who held his rifle in a parrying position across his body. The trick was to go in hard otherwise he could really hurt you. We were told that an earlier recruit had been impaled on his own bayonet because he was too diffident. I escaped with a bruised back as the sergeant helped me on my way. This chap had killed dozens of Chinese soldiers: a sobering thought that helped to concentrate our minds. On a lighter note, I surprised myself, and the arms instructor on the firing range, by scoring high enough to qualify as a marksman. I always suspected afterwards that a stray bullet had enhanced my score.

Towards the end of ten weeks, two of us, myself and Tony Regan a banker, were called to appear before the commanding officer. Both of us were extremely nervous, the Regimental Sergeant Major personally escorted, or rather marched us to the office. We did not know if we were on a disciplinary charge or what was in store for us. Coming up to attention and saluting we faced a young smiling C.O. who immediately told us to stand at ease. 'You two chaps are to be transferred to the Intelligence Corps at Maresfield in Sussex tomorrow, you only came to the Queens to be trained up in case you ever get attached to a fighting regiment. We will be sorry to lose you both because your reports indicate you would be a credit to the Regiment.' He paused: 'Any questions?'

'No thank you sir', we both muttered, somewhat dazed at this sudden change of events.

We were dismissed and as we marched back to our squad the Sergeant Major said : 'Educated f----rs, eh? But you are both alright, just remember what you've learned here and the best of luck'. Then we were off to the Intelligence Corp Headquarters in Maresfield, Sussex, where much to our surprise and disgust we were subjected to an even harsher basic training regime.

Our intake was very varied, ranging from glamorous Highland regiments to technical and light infantry regiments. From among these individuals I was to make some lifetime friends.

We soon learned about the potency of the local vintage *Merrydown Cider*, the local publicans were not allowed to sell more than three small bottles to army personnel.

My fiancé, Annita, and I decided to get married while I was still in the Army and to my surprise I found you have to obtain permission from the Commanding Officer. There was a somewhat startling interview with the Regimental Sergeant Major who was deputising: 'OK laddie, do you really want to get married? If not, we can get you posted no problem'

Quickly catching on to what he assumed was the norm for servicemen getting married in those days of girls being 'up the duff' I said: 'There is no problem sir, we just want to get married'. He smiled with a sorrowful look and said: 'Permission granted, the best of luck – dismissed'.

My stag night was in the pub just outside camp and the landlord relaxed the rule that night. There were two retired Army generals from Scottish regiments, who lived locally, in the bar the same time and, on hearing what the celebration was, insisted on buying all the drinks. Later on they were doing the Sword Dance over carving knives borrowed from the pub kitchen. We were all so drunk that we could not have got past the camp guards without being charged. But these two old soldiers insisted in walking us back to the heavily-guarded gates and called out for the Officer of the Guard. A startled captain came running from the Officers Mess. With a voice born of senior command, one of the Scotsmen barked out: 'Stand down the guard for these soldiers'. Much to his credit and sense of humour the captain issued the order to stand down the guard and we crept into camp not knowing if we had got away with it or not. In fact it was never mentioned and never recorded as far as I know. The Army knows how to look after its own.

Perhaps the most enjoyable experiences were the joint night exercises in the nearby Ashdowne forest with the SAS. I had the dubious distinction of setting part of the forest on fire with a Verry pistol when the flare landed in some dry bracken. Then we were nearly disciplined for dropping off for a bacon and egg breakfast in a village café, after a very arduous night exercise. The trouble was we were fully 'blacked up' and heavily armed and this upset some sensitive soul who complained to the local police. The army public relations officer soothed the aggrieved citizen with the promise that we would be disciplined, though in fact we got away with a tongue in cheek warning.

Then it was off to specialist training in a large country house near Woodhouse Eaves in deepest Leicestershire. I can't remember much about the course but the fantastic cream buns served in the tea breaks still bring a smile to my face. The locals knew we were military, even though we were now out of uniform. One evening in a pub overlooking the River Soar, a group of local youths attacked five of us. That was a mistake because my four companions were SAS types and they pulverised the local yobs. I had kept out of it, leaving it to the experts. These very damaged locals also got charged into the bargain because they were not aware of an enhanced plain-clothes police presence who had witnessed the whole affair.

Our postings were to be Cyprus, Germany or Cheltenham. We actually drew straws to see who would go where. Three of us drew Cheltenham and that meant G.C.H.Q. (Government Communications Headquarters). Alex Colqouhoun and I shared a flat in the grandly-named Montpellier Terrace, not far from the gracious Queens Hotel which looks down on the famous Cheltenham promenade. We were to remain good friends for life. He also made a career in the U.K.A.E.A., albeit as a chemist in Windscale, Cumberland.

After a few weeks we realized that the elegant lady in the flat above us was visited by a very well dressed gentleman several times a week, while her daughter, who was being educated at Cheltenham Ladies College, saw her on the other days. We learned that she had been a senior producer in the BBC, but the arrival of a baby and the resulting scandal, we assumed, caused her to move to Cheltenham.

As for my time in GCHQ, that remains firmly under wraps as decreed by the Official Secrets Acts. However there is a positive spin off. My children and grandchildren are highly impressed that in television parlance, I was in my younger days a 'Spook'!

Chapter 6

After my two years of that enforced break, I was back in Harwell, now married and living in Abingdon with my wife, Annita and a baby son, Andrew.

Not a lot had changed on *ZETA* and I was quickly back in the world of research. Now I found myself working for Dr Alan Gibson, a physicist who drew you into ambitious experiments by his enthusiasm. His remit was to investigate the energy loss processes in *ZETA,* vital to the understanding of how the hot plasma was confined in the magnetic bottle.

One of my tasks was to measure the number of energetic (10 kilovolt) electrons that escaped and hit the stainless steel walls and generated X-Rays utilising a 19th century device, a pinhole camera! We built this ourselves, even down to drilling a one ten thousandth of an inch pin hole in a Beryllium disc. Not an exercise we would repeat today with our modern knowledge of the risks associated with this material.

Then out of the blue something happened that was to have a dramatic effect on my scientific career. In the spring of 1963 my Division Head, the late Bob Wilson (later to become Prof. Sir Robert Wilson, F.R.S., head of the UK Space Program) called me into his office, the windows of which looked out on a panoramic view of the chalk Berkshire Downs.

'Mike', he said, 'It is about a letter from Tom Hughes from Essex University in the latest issue of *Nature.*'

He went on to explain Hughes's idea to use laser light scattering to measure plasma temperatures by measuring the Doppler broadening of the scattered light, akin to the change in pitch as a whistling express train passes you in a station. Put simply, the hotter the plasma the faster the electrons in the plasma move and the colour of the scattered light is more spread out.

'I know very little about lasers so I want you to drop everything else and find out how they work and how powerful they are etc., and come back to me after a couple of weeks research to give me a briefing'. As I got up to leave he said: 'If this Scattering idea looks a starter I have two very bright research fellows starting in a few weeks. David Evans a cosmic ray man from Bristol and Alan DeSilva is an American from The University of Maryland. You three will form the core team'.

It was a steep learning curve but I familiarised myself with some basic laser physics and managed to satisfy Bob Wilson that the newly invented Ruby Laser with some development could form the basis for a tool for scattering. My two new colleagues duly arrived and took up Tom Hughes' idea with great enthusiasm and I soon realised that I was working with two dynamic top class physicists. They not only understood plasma physics but also were hands-on experimentalists with a wide range of skills well suited for the experiment we were about to embark on.

David Evans was the ultimate culture beaver, a consummate reader and theatre fan, especially of the Royal Shakespeare Company productions in Stratford upon Avon.

Often, he and his wife Flo would stay in the Shakespeare Hotel for a week as part of their annual holiday and on one famous occasion they managed to see three plays in a day. He also never owned a car, arguing that he could afford to use a taxi or hire a limousine when he needed to go anywhere. They and their family were to become life-long friends and lived only a few hundred metres away from my home.

Alan DeSilva seemed outwardly to be a quiet bespectacled academic, but he astonished everybody at a Christmas dance by performing a dazzling version of the Charleston. Also as an extra talent, he had inherited his fathers skill as a chutney maker – his father was the State champion of South California. Coupled with a charming American/Japanese wife, Mochigo, he proved to be a colourful addition to the laboratory.

A new custom-built facility for fusion research had been established in nearby Culham a few miles south of Oxford and three miles from Abingdon on Thames, on what had previously been a war time Fleet Air Arm airfield, H.M.S. Hornbill. Aeroplanes operating from there included Sea Harriers, Seafares, Ansons and Reliants. All carried tail identity letters for Culham aircraft, 'CH'.

The U.K.A.E.A. Culham senior staff wanted to create a university atmosphere, even to the extent of building the lab around a series of quadrangles. Then there were the tea rooms, which simulated the old university common rooms. These provided meeting places for all levels of staff, where they could exchange ideas or just gossip. Our particular tea room was run by a lovely Scots lady, Elizabeth, who soon learned about the various individuals drinking habits and their foibles.

Then there was the pressure to publish ones scientific results, which were subject to severe peer refereeing, in the most prestigious scientific journals. In those days publications were the currency of research, not like the conference papers of today.

Indeed, scientists' promotion was heavily dependent on the quality of their published work. This academic atmosphere was further enhanced by having Ph.D. students attached to most experiments, with a dedicated Culham supervisor, as well as the normal University supervisor. This enlightened policy also had the advantage of fostering close relations between Culham and a wide range of Universities, which meant we were to find ourselves in demand as external examiners for Ph.D. vivas.

Our well-connected director had decided that the Culham Laboratory should be opened by an intellectual heavy-weight rather than some non-descript political nominee. Unbeknown to the U.K.A.E.A. Board, he invited his old Cambridge friend, the distinguished scientist and author C. P. Snow to do the honours, without any ceremony. To say this upset Pease's superiors, the U.K.A.E.A. Board, is an understatement, but he never was one to stand on ceremony.

David Evans and I had the pleasure of meeting the great man, he was very affable but seemed somewhat dazed by the lightening tour our Director was subjecting him too.

For the new and ambitious laser scattering experiment we were allocated a large laboratory, and two scientific assistants, and to all respects a blank cheque to carry out a proof of principle experiment to see if Thomson scattering of laser light could be a viable plasma diagnostic.

We calculated the optimum plasma parameters required and hand built a Z-pinch plasma device. This was simply an electrical discharge placed in low-pressure hydrogen in a glass cylinder between two electrodes with a solenoidal magnetic field around it. From scattering theory we determined that by viewing the back scattered laser light from the plasma (electrons) we would observe Doppler broadening of the light which was a direct measure of the electron temperature in the plasma.

Also very significantly there was to be a bonus. If we looked in the opposite direction, that is forward scattering, we could measure the ion temperatures as well, because of the bonding that exists between the electrons and the positive ions.

The laser was to be a more demanding venture because we required the then unheard of power of several megawatts. This was thousands of times more powerful than an electric kettle and was not yet available commercially. Only a very small fraction of the laser light is scattered so high powered lasers are needed to achieve a detectable signal. The only option was a Ruby Laser, not then available commercially to our demanding specification. As a result we had to develop and build our own system. Powerful helical flashtubes were used to 'pump' or 'excite' the atomic levels inside the Ruby laser rods. These Ruby rods were quite beautiful, in those days they had a half inch square cross section and were four inches long with one end cut like a roof-top prism. These crystals are paler in colour than gem quality ruby crystals and were grown synthetically by two competing processes, and even in those days cost thousands of pounds each. The doping of rubies and their optical quality had not yet been optimised so we had to cool the rods with liquid nitrogen to increase the output and devise our own optical switching to get the so-called 'giant pulse'. In fact, we had to switch the laser one thousand times faster than the natural lasing action to overcome background light.

One day we had a visit from our friend, the legendary Charlie Martin from Aldermaston, a world expert on pulse technology and exotic weapon systems. He famously never committed anything to paper in case it was 'leaked'.

His jaw dropped as he looked at our crude set up and said: 'I am very impressed with anybody who can switch in nanoseconds with crocodile clips'. (A nanosecond is one thousandth of a millionth of a second.) He then gave us a master class in fast electronics, which was to stand us in good stead. He then probably returned to Aldermaston to have a chuckle with his colleagues at our expense. But we could not begrudge him that.

In Culham we lacked the measuring equipment to record these very fast laser pulses. However, in the Atomic Weapons Laboratory in Aldermaston a top-secret oscilloscope that was essential for the bomb tests had been developed that was years ahead of any commercial instrument. At a very high level, it was agreed that we could borrow one of these sophisticated devices as long as nobody outside our group could see or touch it. It was delivered in the hours of darkness in a special armed secure vehicle. We were amused when we saw it for the first time because it looked such a crude device, it was housed in a military grey wooden box with a 4-inch cathode ray tube, a couple of knobs on the front and some input electrical plugs on the front. But suffice to say it did the job and really helped us to make rapid progress in the laser development work.

Switching the laser to give a very short pulse was a major technological problem. Initially we used a Kerr cell full of nitro-benzine and a 20,000 volt pulse. These were very unreliable devices and extremely dangerous when they failed, as they would spray cancer inducing droplets as they exploded. So we investigated optical crystals that would rotate the plane of the laser polarised light when a voltage was applied across the crystal.

Our contacts in Aldermaston even offered, for our use only, explosive shutters. These were one way shutters, effectively a glass window that became opaque when an explosive charge was detonated at the outside edge. We did not find this idea attractive.

We had to fall back on some other military scientific friends for their help. This time it was the Royal Radar Establishment in Malvern. This was initially difficult to arrange because their crystal development work was very sensitive at that time. Our well-connected director, Bas Pease, made a few phone calls and in a couple of days we were driving to the establishment in a chauffeured U.K.A.E.A. Authority car to be welcomed by the RRE director. I learned at a very early stage, if you are doing anything of real scientific interest or out of the ordinary, you can punch above your weight in terms of rank and experience.

I mused to myself that some ten years earlier I had joined some engineering college friends for a trip to visit the Morgan Car Works just down the road. We saw the wood framed bodies being hand crafted and potential customers walking down a long row of engines, gearboxes etc and deciding what combination they wanted. What is more, a member of the Morgan family showed us around with a pride that has kept the only British car firm going to this day.

After briefing some very interested R.R.E. senior staff over lunch on our laser scattering work, which was well within their physics compass as they knew all about scattering radio waves off the various atmospheric layers above the earth, they took David Evans and myself to their crystal development laboratory. This was situated in a war-time wooden hut. It looked more like alchemy than science, but they were producing very advanced crystals that could be useful to us. We had expected very clear optical specimens but the one that should work in our laser looked a milky yellow colour. The young enthusiastic physicist thrust a set of unpolished crystals into my hand and said put these in your pocket. He winked and said they were rejects but not to show them to anybody on the way out.

After a very useful visit, I recollect we stopped in a local pub that our driver had tested while David Evans and I were in the lab. On a beautiful sunny evening the three of us enjoyed a meal and the splendid views over the Malvern Hills before returning to Oxfordshire.

This new and very efficient switching greatly improved the performance and our laser could now burn a hole through several razor blades, a somewhat unscientific method of measuring laser power. This was more respectably backed up by calorimeter and pulse width measurements that are normally used to determine the laser output. But it was a good party piece and it also indicated that the laser was well into the megawatts range as a quick check. The other popular trick was to put a coloured balloon inside a clear balloon and when a laser was fired through the balloons only the coloured balloon exploded.

In the course of developing the laser I patented a couple of inventions to protect our ideas rather than for commercial exploitation: 'A device for reducing shimmer adjacent to a Ruby Laser Rod' was one exotic title!

Everybody was fascinated by the new high-powered lasers, even the most illustrious scientists. One day Bas Pease dropped in unannounced with one of the most famous nuclear pioneers, Professor Rudolf Peierls, who had expressed a wish to see a laser in the flesh. In fact he was so interested that he spent an hour with us subjecting us to searching questions on the physics of lasers. We had to strip the laser down so he could see how each part functioned. He was like an enthusiastic schoolboy with a new toy. This was the scientist who assembled the first atomic bomb in Los Alamos, with his own hands, when working on the Manhatten Project.

It is not often we use the word 'magic' in scientific research. But some form of this was required to detect the scattered light that was a millionth of a millionth part of the er beam. To do this we devised sophisticated arrays of les to trap stray laser light, and novel light dumps were to absorb the laser light after it had passed through the plasma, so that specularly reflected light did not saturate the detectors.

A further problem was that we required a very narrow (spectrally) laser line for the ion temperature measurements. In the quest for this we published our very high resolution spectra of the 'giant pulse' in the highly regarded journal *Nature*, helped by D. (Dan) J. Bradley, a young up-and-coming optical physicist from Imperial College, London. Thrilled by this publication, he put his arm around my shoulder and said to me in his strong northern Irish accent: 'Mike, my boy, we are on our way'. He was destined to end up as an Emeritous Professor of Physics at Imperial College, London, and eventually a Fellow of the Royal Society. He would have been inordinately proud to know his son, Professor Donal Bradley, had replicated his success, also at Imperial College.

Once we had obtained the required laser performance, we could at last get on with the experiment. After a few months of intense efforts to optimise the equipment, we were rewarded with the thrill that all explorers enjoy when they experience territory where no man has been before. We could see a scattered light signal above the electronic noise that indicated clear-cut light scattering from electrons and by swinging our collection optics around by 180 degrees we could see a totally different physical effect due to the ions.

The whole experiment turned out to be a total success

and we were able to report, again, in the journal *Nature* for the first time, unambiguous measurements of electron and ion temperatures in a laboratory plasma. This experimental layout was to form the blueprint for all future laser-scattering diagnostic systems in nuclear fusion plasma experiments. It was now possible to measure the key plasma parameters of electron temperature and density that determines the progress towards achieving nuclear fusion as a viable energy source.

In the middle of this excitement, as if to celebrate our success, our daughter Rhian was born in the John Radcliffe Infirmary in Oxford. Our other son Richard was to follow two years later in calmer times.

We then lost our brilliant collaborator, Prof. Alan W. DeSilva, who returned to the United States for a distinguished career. For the next three years David Evans and I explored the potential of laser light scattering. We went on to extend the technique to a wide range of measurements in laboratory plasmas and generally refined this new diagnostic tool. Some sophisticated scattering experiments resulted in two more *Nature* papers

Our breakthrough was widely recognised and the Laser Light Scattering technique was now taken up with great enthusiasm by the rest of the world's Fusion community.

We knew we had had created the essential diagnostic tool to really tackle the problems in creating the conditions for a Nuclear Fusion Reactor.

Chapter 7

During this period, fusion research programmes in general were in the doldrums, with progress handicapped by an apparent limit to how much plasma could be contained. This was called Bohm Diffusion – or in simple terms, excessive plasma leakage from the magnetic bottle. In fact the seeds of doubt were beginning to set in, maybe laboratory nuclear fusion was not feasible after all.

However, there was one notable exception to this general air of gloom – The Russian Tokamak T3 device in Moscow. Academician Lev Artsimovitch reported that it had excellent plasma confinement and claimed very high plasma temperatures of around 10 million degrees Celsius. This news was received with considerable scepticism by fusion laboratories outside the Soviet Bloc, especially the Americans. In some quarters it was thought the objections were politically motivated. However, I have since had the opportunity to speak to many of the main Fusion players in the USA and I have found this was not generally the case. The prime reason for their concerns was that the Russian results were so contrary to their own experimental experiences and also at variance to the then current theoretical predictions. In those days the theorists held considerable sway and whatever they pronounced was taken as the considered wisdom on the subject.

Stung by this lack of recognition by the non-communist world, Lev Artsimovitch invited a senior delegation of

U.K.A.E.A. Culham scientists to see the *Tokamak* work in Moscow and ask for help in confirming their results.

This invitation to the British was largely due to his long-standing friendship with R.S. (Bas) Pease which had blossomed from their contacts after the declassification of *ZETA*. Bas Pease was a direct descendant of Edward Pease, the founder of the Fabian movement, which was to lead to the formation of the modern Labour Party. This socialist family background, I suspect, gave him an aura of respectability in the eyes of the Soviet Communist Party officials.

Culham sent a very senior delegation headed by Sir John Adams, who had been brought in from CERN in Geneva to boost the UK fusion work. My future boss Nicol Peacock accompanied them to talk about the various methods that could be used to confirm the *Tokamak* parameters. It transpired that Artsimivitch had been very impressed by our pioneering Culham laser scattering work and he asked if the U.K.A.E.A. would send a team to Moscow to measure the electron temperature and density of the *Tokamak* plasma.

Given the level of mistrust between the Eastern and Western blocs at that time, he must have been a man of immense influence to convince his political masters that such a visit was essential, as it was tacitly admitting that the UK had a technical lead over the Soviet Union in the measurement of plasma parameters.

The British participation was approved at the highest level of the United Kingdom Atomic Authority. I suspect our Division Head, K. V. (Keith) Roberts, put the case for collaboration with the Russians to the Culham management committee very much 'tongue in cheek'. When he had previously worked in Aldermaston he had been responsible for creating the sophisticated computer code that led to the optimization of the British Hydrogen bomb. Also on the Culham management committee was Bryan Taylor, the Head of Theory Division, who was behind the 'Bomb' calculations.

It is worth recording verbatim an interview he (now Professor Bryan Taylor F.R.S.) gave for the Princeton (USA) Fusion History Project. In this he explains how he first became involved with Controlled Nuclear Fusion work.

' – – – and then suddenly out of the blue in the Autumn of 1957 the opportunity suddenly arose. My supervisor, Corner, called me into his office one day and said: "Bryan, you've done all this wonderful work on radio flash (EMP), so you know all about Maxwell's Equations." (Laugh) "Well, would you tell your supervisor that you don't know about Maxwell's Equations?" So I said: "Yes sir, I understand all about Maxwell's equations". (We called our Division heads "Sir" in those days.) He said: "Oh good, because the people in Harwell", which was a rival establishment some twenty miles away, "are going to announce that they've got nuclear fusion in a machine called *ZETA* and its going to make power for everybody for next to nothing – from seawater. It is important that we get on this project because if there is a test ban we might need some diversification. We are well placed to work on neutron blankets, and we are experts on neutron scattering and

interactions and know more than anyone (in the UK) about 14MeV neutrons (Laugh) We can work on materials blankets, but we must have somebody who understands the core of the thing which depends on magnetic fields. You and Keith (Roberts) can familiarize yourselves with all that stuff and be the theory division advisors on this great new world of magnetic fusion." '

Barth (the interviewer): 'This conversation was essentially the beginning of your interest in plasma physics?'

Taylor: 'Absolutely. The day it all started was in Corners office, telling me that Harwell were going to announce they'd got nuclear fusion in this magnetic device called *ZETA*, and Aldermaston needed people who understood it.'

There were a few more hurdles to clear before we received the all clear, but very soon the Anglo-Russian mission received the blessing of the Foreign Office and The Department of Technology, in those days headed by the Minister, Wedgewood Benn. We never got to hear if there was any opposition to the project, but we could not imagine such a scheme in those political fraught times would go through 'on the nod.'

Because of the great sensitivity of the project it was to be led by a senior scientist Nicol Peacock, a highly respected spectroscopist. The team consisted of myself, Peter Wilcock, a brilliant technical innovator, and the youngest member, Derek

Robinson, who was about to be posted for thirteen months with his wife Marion, to work at the Kurchatov Institute in Moscow.

Only Derek and myself had any Thomson scattering experience. However, his invitation to Moscow was based on his theoretical ability, which counted very highly on the scale of things in the Russian scientific establishment.

It could hardly have been a more disparate team in terms of personalities. Nicol Peacock, a bearded wiry Scotsman, who cultivated a 'hard man' imge. Weaned on single malt whiskeys and the Robert Burns culture, he was also a graduate of the Liverpool University mountaineering club. He had impressed his fellow young bucks in his earlier Aldermaston bachelor days by his mode of transport. Not for him a MG or Triumph sports car but a van with a mattress in the back!

Peter Wilcock was also an ex-Aldermaston man, a natural sportsman, best described as burly, he had rowed for his university. A perfectionist in whatever he took on as a hobby or work, it had to be the best, to a fault, and I never knew him defeated by a technical problem. It would have been difficult to find a more competent all round experimental scientist to work with.

Then there was Derek Robinson, destined for an outstanding scientific career. He was of slim build and a great fell walker and traveller, but somewhat brash about his competence in all scientific matters, despite him being the youngest member of the team. From a military family he had a catholic taste in books and the arts. His health was to prove a problem. The Russian doctor who gave him the compulsory medical required for foreign workers, failed him because of a duodenal ulcer. But Derek refused to return to the UK, having decided to tough it out.

In contrast, I had a more relaxed approach to life, sport was to be enjoyed rather than taken too seriously. In the laboratory I had a pragmatic approach to experiments and increased the probability of success by reducing the number of unnecessary complications. Perhaps my strongest point was the ability to draw on a wide range of people and capitalize on their expertise and drive a project along. One of the original networkers you could say. A very successful female ex-student said to me: 'You were fun to work with'. Probably because some of our proof of principle experiments could have graced the children's television program Blue Peter. Such apparently primitive arrangements sometimes raised the eyebrows of the purists, but the results always seemed to justify the means.

Chapter 8

The project really came to life in December 1968 when Peter Wilcock and myself were invited by the Russian State Committee for Science to visit the Kurchatov Institute as the first phase of the collaboration, to plan the whole enterprise. This had been approved, or at least 'rubber stamped' by Leonid Brezhnev in the final year of his premiership.

In those days the Russian Embassy in London would not issue entry visas until the very last minute. The Foreign Office duty officer telephoned us to say we would not get the visas until midnight before we were due to fly, which was not exactly good for the nerves. On the stroke of midnight, like a character out of the James Bond films, a Foreign Office motorbike courier, completely dressed in black, roared up on to our drive, saluted and handed over the crucial documents, which suitably impressed my children who had waited up especially for the occasion.

Peter and I were driven to Heathrow Airport by the Director's uniformed chauffeur. I think other passengers must have wondered who we were to command his smart military salute as we left him to enter the departure hall.

In those days we flew out to Moscow on a BEA (British European Airways) flight. As we taxied in after landing we were very surprised to see a uniformed BEA official, standing to attention in freezing conditions and saluting the plane. This was apparently because of the Royal Mail status of the flight, and indeed there was the Royal insignia emblazoned on the fuselage. But more to the point apparently, it impressed the Russians to 'beat hell' a diplomat told me. Such was the state of East-West relations at that time that countries played such mind games.

The elevated status of the collaboration struck us immediately when we were met at Sherametavo Airport by a young physicist, Volodiya Sannikov, who was to work with us. He came with a chauffeured government limousine ready to whisk us to central Moscow. It was the first time Peter and I had experienced really low air temperatures. It was a breath stopping minus 30 degrees Celsius. The Russians fussed about, insisting that we should put the ear flaps down on our recently purchased fur hats in case we got frostbite. Shortly after leaving the airport, Volodiya pointed out a tangle of girders by the roadside that was a sombre memorial and a grim reminder as to how close the Germans had been to entering Moscow. As we drove along the wide highway we had our first sight of the massive Stalinist style buildings that lined the route into the city centre.

We were dropped off at the Hotel Budapest just around the corner from the Bolshoi Theatre. The hot air from the hotel changed to steam as it billowed out of the open doors to meet the sulphurous central Moscow city atmosphere. Faded grandeur, best describes the ambience of the hotel. This was offset by very impressive chandeliers and a glittering very extensive dining room. It was packed with very high-ranking military officers, their uniforms covered in red and gold and rows of decorations, many with glamorous female companions, but a few with more ample ladies who were probably their wives.

All the tables were occupied, but two Russian full generals beckoned for us to sit at two spare seats at their table. They looked visibly shaken when they realised we were English, but called to a tardy waitress to serve us before making a speedy exit, leaving behind an almost full bottle of very good Georgian wine to which we did full justice. A substantial borsch, followed by some sour cream and fruit concoction, satisfied our appetite. We looked around, taking in the atmosphere, and said to each other 'this really is Russia'. So it was. Old ladies, sat at the top of every corridor watching all the comings and goings. The bedrooms were basic but we slept well.

The next morning we were picked up by Dennis Ivanov, the Chief Physicist/Engineer, who was responsible for the design and construction of the *Tokamak T3*. He took us to very wintry and deserted *Park of Achievements* for a quick tour. The highlight was being able to actually touch astronaut Gagarin's space capsule, which must have been unbelievably uncomfortable. There was a most elaborate leather harness, which must have served to anchor him securely in what is best described as a large canon ball

Impressed, but feeling thoroughly frozen, we retired to an empty restaurant and after several tumblers of the best Vodka we thawed out. Dennis took the opportunity to educate us about the properties and virtues of the various Vodkas. Over lunch we notionally fitted our proposed diagnostic on to a sketch of the *Tokamak* he made on the table in lieu of the engineering drawings, it was a good civilised start to our venture.

In the evening we met up with Derek and Marion Robinson in their flat close to the Kurchatov Institute. They had been out there for just a month, time to find out the basic facts of living in Soviet Russia at the height of the cold war. Marion in particular had time to find out how to locate food and how to survive in the fairly tough circumstances that existed at that time.

She was to prove invaluable in keeping us together in body and soul and mixed freely with the locals, she was even invited into the local schools to describe the British way of life. She had sacrificed a year of her career in Harwell as a chemist to accompany Derek on his Moscow attachment. No mean scientist herself, her professional competence is reflected in the fact she was one of the few British scientists entrusted to analyse the first sample of moon dust brought back to earth.

The following day, we made our first visit to the Kurchatov Institute, situated in an orchard in the suburbs of Moscow. Here we were in what was previously known as Laboratory No. 2, a very bland title for an establishment that had played such a major role in Soviet nuclear physics since 1943, particularly in the development of nuclear weapons. This Soviet equivalent of Harwell was situated just beyond the city Belt Railway line, a kilometre from the Moskva River.

Kurchatov himself chose the site on the edge of the former Khodynskoye Field, which for many decades served as an artillery and machine gun proving ground. This was to be the Institute of Atomic Energy.

Somewhat to our surprise we were admitted with just a nod from the security guards instead of the rigorous procedures we were subjected to when entering secure U.K. establishments. Once inside it was very much like Aldermaston with fenced areas within other fences, which we took to contain the more sensitive projects such as nuclear submarine reactors. We had decided amongst ourselves not to show any interest or curiosity in anything except what was related our own area of work. In other words we did not want to 'rock the boat' in those sensitive times.

We were warmly received by Slava Strelkov, the *Tokamak T3* Group Leader, a fair-headed, athletic-looking man with distinctive Slavic features. He made it very clear we were to get total support in the forthcoming task. It was a bit of a culture shock to see the *Tokamak T3* device. It was obviously built to be purely functional with no concession to aesthetics. Only surfaces or components were precision finished that needed to be. However, who were we to criticize? It was more successful than any other such device in the world.

It soon became apparent that there would be a lot of problems to overcome. Some are described here to give the reader some idea of the realities of experimental physics. The challenge was to identify them in the short time we had there. For a start the Torus was baked to a high temperature to ensure a very high vacuum. This would distort our vacuum windows and lens assemblies.

Peter had a severe grilling from the Russian tec people regarding the compatibility of the materials we planned to use: vacuum sealing techniques, window compatibility, etc.

They were surprised we could produce metal to glass seals of 50mm diameter, essential to provide windows large enough to efficiently collect the scattered laser light. It also became apparent we would need to have protective in-vacuo shutters in place to prevent the windows becoming obscured due to metallic sputtering during the machine cleaning process.

We were able to convince them that we would need to build-in a lot of precautions to control electrical interference and external magnetic field leakage and that we had the expertise to do this. Peter Wilcock was a leading authority in these areas and I think the Russians were very impressed by his knowledge and confidence to sort out these problems.

The mains voltage supply was prone to dropping by 30 or so volts. There was some amusement when Slava Strelkov told us that one day when the reduced voltage was affecting the *Tokamak* performance, Artsimovich, who was around at the time, was so annoyed that he telephoned the local power-station manager and told him to put more coal in the furnaces to increase the voltage output. This had the desired effect, but Peter and I made a mental note that we had better be prepared for that scenario.

Also, there was a lot of electrical noise generated by the experiment that would have swamped the low scattered signals we anticipated from our detectors. Slow rising stray magnetic fields had prevented the Russians using photomultiplier detectors nearer than four metres and would pose a serious risk to the operation of our photomultipliers. And, as we would have to place them within one metre of the torus, very effective screening would be required.

The port we planned to mount our re-entrant optics on was prone to collapse by several millimetres under vacuum, which would have misaligned or damaged the critical light collection system. So we would have to design our collection optics accordingly.

As soon as we went to the basement under the *Tokamak* where our laser would be mounted, we could feel severe vibrations under our feet from the huge flywheel generators that powered the *T3* machine. The sand under the concrete floors had sunk leaving the floors to act like the skin of a drum. Without suitable precautions it would have been impossible to keep the laser aligned, let alone direct the laser beam accurately through the collimating light baffles that controlled the stray light levels

These were just a few of the problems we would have to sort out when we returned to the U.K.

Then of course was the thorny issue of the background light levels emitted by the plasma. We needed to know this to calculate the laser power required to obtain measurable scattered light signals. John Sheglov, their senior spectroscopist, had made absolute measurements to determine these levels which he reported as being very low because of the low impurity content of the plasma. Little did we realize at that time that this issue was a time bomb laying in wait for us!

Chapter 9

We returned to Culham with copious notes and several sketches. These contained Peter's review of technical problems and my outline schematic for the optics of the scattering experiment. For some reason or other the *T3* team did not seem to have many engineering drawings of the *Tokamak*. In fact we came back with just one detailed drawing of a vacuum port that we would be mounting our collection optics on.

Then we set about to make the project a reality. We were committed to delivering a complete working system by mid-April 1969 – three months to solve the problems and build the most advanced scattering system that had been attempted up to that time.

However we did have one great advantage. Our Director, Bas Pease, had secured for us top priority with access to all the U.K.A.E.A. resources. In those days the Atomic Weapons Establishment, Aldermaston, was part of the U.K.A.E.A. and we knew we would have to exploit our contacts there to drive the project through and on time. For years we had built up a totally unofficial mutual help ethic with the Weapons Trial Section, which developed into personal friendships.

In particular with the group leader, Bill Waller, who had established his reputation with the high-speed rotating mirror (400,000 rpm) camera. He was the consummate professional engineer, demanding perfection from his staff, workshops and from manufacturers. It was interesting walking around his area. It seemed to be populated with miniature submarines with massive arrays of lights and many other strange objects. We knew better than to ask what these items were for. Bill was a bachelor, a bit on the chubby side, due probably to him living with his widowed mother who spoilt him. I was always amused by the way his office walls were covered with his certificates and memberships of various engineering institutes, not the normal practice in the Authority.

Almost incongruously in comparison, for most of the optical components we depended on W. H. (Bill) Ball, the optical manager of Keeler Optical Ltd, who made specialised equipment for the opthalmic industry. The factory was situated in a tree-lined street in the suburbs of Windsor on the opposite side of the River Thames to Windsor Castle.

Since our very first scattering experiments in 1964, he had been enthusiastically making specialised optical components in very short turn around times. This provided an enjoyable diversion from his normal work. The directors of Keelers seemed happy to go along with this arrangement. Bill, an affable, sandy haired, wiry man was a low handicap golfer and was often invited to play in the most exclusive golf clubs in the Oxon, Berks and Bucks triangle. He could also have been a county cricketer but family pressures forced him to go for a more stable occupation. Again this developed into a personal friendship that included our wives and we enjoyed many meals together in some of the most pleasant pubs and restaurants in the glorious Chilterns

At the heart of the experiment were the 'red sensitive' photomultipliers, which were used to detect the scattered light. We needed the highest possible sensitivity because of the very low light levels scattered from the plasma. Over the years Peter Crab, the RCA European Manager, had supplied us with state of the art military specification photomultipliers and ours were always specially selected. In fact we often had the pick before the military customers because Peter became so involved with our work. He became a good friend and he also used to look forward to lunches, his favourite being the thatched roofed *Barley Mow* in nearby Clifton Hampden, made famous in the novel and the film *Three Men in a Boat,* when it was still a traditional inn.

I don't think the other customers there realised that the glass tubes we were scrutinising were the latest thing in United States military hardware.

Years later, I was to find myself in the same pub with a trio of American Air Force Colonels from military research establishments on entirely different business.

Logistics proved to be a major task, most of which was handled by our chief technician, Harry Jones, a redoubtable Liverpudlian with superb man management talent. He had been the chief electrician on the Cunard Line, which mightily impressed David Evans and myself on Harry's recruitment interview. In fact we overruled two senior engineers on the board who thought he was not professional enough for their tastes. Probably one of the best decisions we ever made.

Football was his first love after his family and he used to run the Culham football team. This had one very large advantage in that the players came from many key parts of the lab, especially the manufacturing side. This meant that anything we wanted built enjoyed a very high priority in Culham's very sophisticated workshops

One serious problem that could have jeopardised the whole project was the embargo on exporting strategic equipment to sensitive countries, i.e. Russia and China. Critical to the success of the experiment were the military RCA photomultipliers with extended red performance. These were on the banned list.

Peter Wilcock and I pragmatically applied the old security adage – 'the need-to-know-principle' to our advantage. We simply described them as high gain photomultipliers in the shipping list, which was technically true. In the event nobody was any the wiser and there was no harm done and more to the point we had the best detectors possible.

Another problem that could have scuppered the whole experiment was the bright flash of light emitted during the forming of a *Tokamak* plasma. This would have disabled the photomultipliers or at least made them unreliable. This was in the days before the tubes could be electronically switched on and off, so we had to provide an extremely fast mechanical external shutter. Peter Wilcock came up with a simple but brutal solution, mounting a slotted blade on the end of a camera shutter drive solenoid which he pulsed by discharging a large capacitor into the coil. The speed of this shutter widely exceeded any other mechanical shutter available. Testing of this device was exciting, some of the prototype blades becoming projectiles. But the final design that overcame this problem did have one idiosyncrasy, which was to cause some amusement to Lev Artsimovitch a few months later in Moscow.

The very large amplitude floor vibrations, that we knew we would have to counter for the sake of laser stability, were solved by Peter with what was a very effective anti-vibration mount. This was essential for the laser to be sited amongst the machinery in the basement below the *T3* machine. On top of massive concrete benches he placed alternative layers of rubber and lead for the laser optical benches to rest on. He also solved the problem of penetrating magnetic fields by shielding the photomultipliers in concentric cylinders of low and high-saturation u-metal. These are metals that absorb magnetic fields very effectively. This shielding was improved further by mounting it all in a soft iron outer case.

Peter had also persisted in his demand for an electrically screened room, or Faraday cage, for the recording equipment. We decided to take the best one possible, i.e. a Siemens, and how essential that was to prove. The next headache was to provide flexibility in the solid copper screening for the cables between the screened room and the moveable measuring equipment trolley. Again Peter demonstrated from earlier experimentation that carefully cleaned compression fittings normally used for water supply could provide the near perfect electrical contact necessary for electrical screening. This compression-jointed copper pipe snake gave the necessary flexibility with excellent electrical screening.

Some might argue that this is too much technical detail but it is worth recording because every facet was critical to the ultimate success of the experiment. Hopefully, it might give an indication to those readers outside scientific research what an experiment actually involves.

The optical design was my domain. I devised a novel set of prismatic lenses that could be scanned by a periscopic arrangement to carry out spatially resolved temperature and density measurements across the plasma radius. Fundamental to the success of any scattering experiment is the suppression of stray laser light, which could swamp the very small signals we were looking for. Based on the principles that David Evans and I had evolved over several scattering experiments in Culham, I incorporated the laser beam collimator and the beam energy dump which featured special optical filter glass with very high absorption at the laser wavelength.

Likewise the spectrometer and fibre optics multi-channel system used to analyse the scattered light spectrum were adapted from our well-proven designs. A powerful helium-neon laser was built into the ruby laser bench to facilitate alignment of the main laser beam to ensure it passed centrally through the critical array of glass apertures and then through the centre of the plasma.

We had been heavily dependent on fibre optics in all our earlier scattering experiments in Culham. I had pioneered their use in the early sixties in conjunction with an old established firm in Glasgow, Barr and Stroud, who, despite an old fashioned image, were on the leading edge of military hardware, much of it top secret.

My collaborator there was a glass scientist, John Ballantine, who had developed the special glass radomes that protect aircraft radar antennae. He had seen the potential of optical fibres from the very start and we were able to try out some of the first samples he made. They were to be the solution of the biggest problem in optical diagnostics, that is, the transfer of light from one point to another with the minimum of loss in the process.

Perhaps their most lucrative business was the supply and maintenance of the highly classified periscopes for the Royal Navy's fleet of nuclear submarines. On our visits to their factory in Anniesland, Glasgow, David Evans and I were not allowed to look through these periscopes. It seems there was special classified instrumentation built into to these massive devices, which we could only speculate on. Barr and Stroud also did very well out of straightening out the periscopes, which were bent when the submarine captains tried to surface through thick Arctic ice.

One secret they did let us into was the final test for the periscopes before they were returned to the Royal Navy. If the testers could see the markings on cows in a field some four miles away then they passed muster.

We must have been considered as valued customers because we were always accorded lunch in the Directors dining room. The waitress used to come in to our meeting room to take our order, which was a full silver and white-linen service affair. The directors had their serviette rings engraved with their names but visitors had plain rings. The whole firm exhibited a touch of class in all its activities.

Over lunch David and I noted with amusement the

Directors pre-occupation with golf and how impressed they were that we both lived very close to the famous Oxfordshire Frilford Golf Club.

In our planning prior to our visit to Moscow in the previous December, the Russian *Tokamak* team had assured us that the background light emitted from the plasma was very low due to the very clean plasma. As mentioned earlier, this had been confirmed by photometric measurements carried out by their senior spectroscopist. This gave us enough confidence to use a relaxation mode ruby laser that has a pulse length of a millisecond or so. This, we thought, would give a lot of photons to play with.

But Peter Wilcock, in particular, felt we should build in a 'q' switching facility that gives a very short 20 to 30 nanosecond pulse that we had historically used in all our Culham experiments. This was in case the background light was higher than the Russians believed. Our senior management, who were in awe of anything Russian, ridiculed the idea and forbade us to provide this extra equipment.

I agreed with Peter. We went ahead with our 'press on regardless policy' and sneaked in the fast amplifiers, which Peter had designed in record time, and also the other fast switching components. Little did we know then but this was to prove to be one of the most important decisions we made.

Our old friend Bill Waller and his weapons trials team in Aldermaston had taken up the challenge with great enthusiasm and built all the optical equipment for us in record time, even by Weapons standards. Bill Ball, at Keeler Optics in Windsor, worked around the clock to manufacture the demanding optical components critical to the whole experiment

Even the packing required special consideration because of the delicate nature of all the equipment. Specialist packing agents LEP, tailor made 26 cases with 'floated' inner boxes. This was a very costly exercise, but it paid off, not a single item was lost or damaged in the journey to Moscow.

We had pressed hard to take a Siemens screened room to get over the electrical noise problems. But even in its flat packed form it required an aircraft with a 2.5 metre wide cargo hold door. It turned out the only civilian aircraft flying into Moscow that satisfied that criteria was a Pakistan Airlines Boeing 707. This flight was only once a week so we had to make sure we could book it for March and that the airline was happy with our unusual load. In fact the airline was very co-operative and enthusiastic beyond the call of duty.

About three weeks before we were due to leave for Moscow, Bas Pease called me to his office for a chat, as he put it. 'Mike, old chap,' he said. 'I've been thinking. The reputation of the Laboratory and in fact UK science rests on you lot pulling off the scattering experiment in Moscow. You are the person with the most extensive scattering experience so you must have the best feel for the feasibility of the whole exercise. I know it is not really a fair thing to put this on you, but we can pull the plug on the collaboration if you have any doubts at all'. He paused and said: 'Whatever you say, either way, is totally between us and I would totally respect your judgement and not hold it against you whatever the outcome'.

In hindsight, I probably replied a shade too quickly –

being high on adrenaline. I hardly considered the question before replying. 'I think we have the technical aspects covered and there is a high degree of flexibility built in., so I think we should go for it.'

'Fine,' Bas said. 'But I think you are bloody brave'. That was it, the point of no return and there was nothing left between us and setting off for the great adventure in Moscow.

Interestingly, a barrister friend thinks I should not reveal this confidential conversation. However as 'transparency' is the over-riding consideration these days I have included it for the record.

It was many years later before I mentioned to Nicol Peacock that Bas Pease had given me the opportunity to halt the project in its tracks. He was astonished and initially quite upset that the final decision had been taken out of his hands. After a while he conceded that he would have to defer to my considerable experience and background knowledge on the laser scattering technique. Although a world class scientist, he had no experience of Laser Scattering techniques. It had been a straight-forward scientific judgement by Bas Pease and myself, too important to consider anybody's personal feelings.

Chapter 10

The intensive three months preparation had been very stressful for our families, particular Peter and I, both with young children, but now the tension was heightened by our imminent departure to Moscow.

Then there I was, on 16th March 1969, boarding the PIA 707 at Heathrow Airport having been bussed up to the green-and-white liveried aeroplane. There was a cluster of ground staff with their specialised loading equipment in front of the abnormally large cargo hold doors. I stood with the other passengers on a freezing windblown Heathrow tarmac feeling pretty lonely. At the last minute, Peter Wilcock had been laid low by a kidney infection and had to delay his departure. Standing on top of the aircraft steps I turned to wave to the Culham Stores Officer, Des Constable, who had come especially to supervise the loading of the 26 packing cases containing our experiment, weighing some 5 tons in all. He waved back and mouthed 'best of luck'.

The flight arrived in Moscow Sheremetevo Airport which was covered in a deep fresh snow that made for a nasty landing. In fact the aircraft slewed the last few hundred metres of runway sideways. I was very relieved to be met by Volodiya Sannikov and Derek Robinson after I had made a rapid transit through passport control and customs formalities thanks to my diplomatic visa.

Later in the Kurchatov Institute, I was greeted by Slava Strelkov and most of the *T3* team. Shavranov, their top plasma theorist, came in and introduced himself. 'I know you Englishmen cannot function without your tea breaks,' he said. 'I will provide the means.' An hour later he struggled in beaming and carrying a large silver samovar. Such was to be our welcome.

Nicol Peacock, Peter Wilcock and I had been allocated a large guest flat in Yul Rogova, within walking distance of the Kurchatov Institute. This had three bedrooms and a large lounge. It felt somewhat spartan, fitted out in what reminded us of post-war utility furniture in the UK, but comfortable enough for the time we were going to spend in it. This was in the same block as Derek and Marion's smaller flat and it also housed many of the lab's employees. The flats were very warm, heated by the excess heat piped from the infamous local power station.

This suburb of Moscow, except for the Kurchatov Institute, was purely residential, made up of blocks of identical apartment blocks with a few basic shops. It was a Metro journey and a short bus trip from central Moscow. A redeeming feature was that the River Moskva was only a ten minute walk away from our flat and what could have passed as a beach was popular with the locals for picnics on sunny weekends. One Sunday morning, I remember walking down the road to spend a few hours there in the sun and the sound of BBC's Family Favourites signature tune drifted out of the windows of a flat. A surreal experience, but I missed the Abingdon church bells of St.Nicolas and St. Helens.

I had a day to settle myself in the laboratory because the heavy snowfall had given the airport staff trouble in handling our equipment and this was to cause it to arrive a day late in the Kurchatov Institute. I was sorting out my notebooks etc., in the spacious office we had been allocated, when Academician, Lev Artsimovitch, came in smiling. 'Ah! Michael, John, welcome to Moscow. I hope everything goes well for you. Let me know if you want anything and I will help you. And how is my friend Bas Pease? I will telephone him and report that the equipment and you have arrived safely.'

I thought I detected a twinkle in his eye as I mentally noted he had put the equipment before me. Then we had a general chat, but before leaving he said: 'Michael, John, remember all of us Russians are basically peasants and are not at all sophisticated. This is reflected in our beloved proverbs, which are often very basic and often crude'. I don't know if he had expected our team to be all sophisticates like Bas Pease, because I thought at the time it was a strange thing for him to say.

I was very impressed by that conversation because, after all, Lev Artsimovitch was the chief Russian scientist when Soviet science was probably at its peak and he had sought me out to show his support for us in our endeavours. On reflection I realised that he was very dependent on our carrying out a successful experiment because he had made such a bold move in inviting us to Moscow.

It seemed strangely familiar to go into the *Tokamak T3* control room. It was very reminiscent of the *ZETA* control room that I had spent so much time in back in Harwell. Once I had tuned in to the countdown and background chat in Russian, I could imagine being back in Harwell in Hangar 7. I was struck straight away by how few staff were involved compared with *ZETA*, in fact everything was being carried out with a fraction of the resources we were accustomed to in the U.K.A.E.A..

Then it was into action. Derek and I were joined by Volodiya who was to prove invaluable as the link-man between us and the Russians. With some enthusiastic technicians, we unpacked the cases and started to assemble various parts of the experiment. To my relief, Peter Wilcock arrived a few days later after recovering from the illness that had delayed his departure. He made an immediate impact on the progress, especially on the electrical and electronic side.

Our Russian colleagues, we discovered, also enjoyed their tea breaks. The trouble was that their lunch was often two or more hours later than we were used to, so it was often six in the evening before we congregated in Slava Strelkovs office for the afternoon break. Packets of biscuits materialised and the samovar went into overdrive and the intelligentsia of the Soviet fusion physics would drift in for a chat. The affable, short, bearded Fillipov sported three Lenin medals for his bomb work, somebody enlightened us without any further explanation. His wife, who had her own experimental group, was often joined by Asa Razomova, a very well known lady plasma physicist. Most days Kodomtsev the distinguished theoretician would join the company. He kept a genial fatherly eye on us and seemed to enjoy our company and a 'good chat'. I must admit I was somewhat in awe of this renowned scientist, but one evening he told me that he was very impressed by us experimentalists. 'You are the people who make ideas work,' he said. I think he really meant it and it made me feel good to receive such a heartfelt compliment.

Boris Kodomtsev liked to illustrate his lectures with cartoons and he had a field-day with us visitors as can be seen in the examples of his humour and artistic licence that I have included in this book. He was destined to be the next Director of the Kurchatov Institute.

I asked the Tokamak Group leader Slava Strelkov how he became involved with Fusion work. He explained to me it was down to the good old communist system of directed labour, the top physics students were drafted in to work on the then fledgling topic. Prior to that he would have ended up on Weapons research, though of course the initial motivation for the Nuclear Fusion work was not that innocent because of its potential as a neutron source.

The Russian *Tokamak* team had made a good job of the massive concrete benches to support the ruby laser and input optics to be located in the noisy, dark and oil fume filled basement. A glamorous blonde lady welder turned up to demolish some handrails that prevented craning the benches down below – and then welded them back afterwards to their previous form after we had manoeuvred the unwieldy optical mounts into their allotted positions.

Chapter 11

We quickly acclimatised ourselves to the day-to-day Russian life, with Marion Robinson keeping us together in body and soul and finding out where we could find the basics that had to be purchased. Every Saturday morning we would go to the hard currency shop (Berioska) where even kilogram tins of the best Beluga caviar could be bought. There was always a huge selection of amber jewellery as this was one of Russia's natural resources. My wife soon reached saturation point with this. The cameras and binoculars were very good value, though they tended to be heavier and not so well finished as their western counterparts. Connoisseurs of vodka were well served and there were some excellent Georgian brandies and wines that stood comparison with the best French labels. The difference between these hard currency shops and the ordinary shops that most Moscovites had to use was immense. The latter reminded me of my childhood days during World War Two and the shortages. We explored the covered market where peasants came in from the surrounding villages with often quite meagre offerings.

The giant department store GUM only served to accentuate the paucity of goods available to the Soviet citizens. The famous toyshop, Detsky Mir, with its remarkable art deco architecture, was somewhat better, probably due to the Russians love of children. This meant that Peter and I were able to buy some quite unusual toys for our children. The other thing that the Russians did well was to produce very attractive postage stamps. This was of course to bring in much needed hard currency. For those just interested in the themes and designs this was ideal but not as a financial investment because they produced too many.

One thing that struck me was the great kindness of every Russian I came across. For example they are neurotic about frostbite with good reason. But I was quite often stopped in the street by passers-by who would point my ears and warn 'obmorozhenie!!' (frost bite), because I always tended to have dry skin on my ear lobes. My Russian was not up to explaining that, so I just used to thank the stranger graciously and pull my hat flaps further down.

One thing I learned about the Russian winter was that when the children were not playing outside it was really dangerously cold. Although, if there was no wind, they seemed to enjoy the outdoors whatever the temperature.

Another public-spirited action, which I could not imagine happening in our country, was commonplace on the buses or the trams. The bus fare was 4 kopecks, but on trams for some reason it was only 3 kopecks. If you did not have the correct change the surrounding passengers would all chip in to help you put in only the exact fare. I was embarrassed one day in a tram when I went to put in 4 kopecks. A high-ranking Red Army officer grabbed my hand and said: 'That is too much,' and organised the correct money for me.

On occasions I ran into trouble in the local shops near

the Kurchatov Institute. The common Soviet practice was to buy a ticket for the item you wanted to purchase from a cashier, but sometimes when you reached the counter the item you wanted had gone or the ticket did not match what you wanted. But every time the housewives in the shop, who had spotted me straight away, because there were virtually no foreigners in that area, would dash to the rescue, scolding the hapless shop assistant. They always seemed to want to know where I had bought my overcoat? How much did it cost? And how many children did I have? I did not like to tell them I had blown all my foreign cold weather allowance on it in Walters, the superior tailors in Turl Street, Oxford, as it would have probably represented a couple of months salary, or more, for an ordinary Muscovite citizen

We were struck by the number of drunks lying totally unconscious in the Moscow streets in sub zero temperatures. We were told that lorries toured around a few times a day, and the police would throw the unfortunates into the open back and then deposit them a few miles outside the city limits to sober up. Asking if this doesn't have fatal results, we were told laconically that their veins are so full of alcohol that the cold does not affect them.

Even in the early days, Marion was concerned about Derek's health. He was driving himself to the limit between working with us on the scattering experiment and his own theoretical work in the evenings. It seems the Russians too had a lot of health problems. There was even a special dining area for those with stomach or digestive problems. At lunch times, some of our *T3* colleagues used to part company with us to have their special diets in a separate canteen. The meals were certainly substantial, designed I think to combat the cold weather. Huge quantities of meat and potatoes seemed to be the norm but I could never take to the sour cream desserts that seemed to be the favourite dish.

It took about three weeks to install the whole experiment, which also involved opening up the torus to fit the re-entrant collection window assembly, input window and laser beam collimator. Then the laser dump section, which absorbed the laser beam after it had passed through the plasma, was mounted on top of the machine. The Russian technicians enjoyed putting up the Siemens screened room that housed all the Cathode Ray Tektronics Oscillosopes to record the anticipated scattering signals. In the same constricted space we had to fit in our electronics that fired the laser and link our equipment in with the *Tokamak T3* system. They were falling over themselves to help in all ways and very keen to see the state-of-the-art equipment we had brought with us. They were visibly pleased at the degree to which we included them. This encouraged them to play a pro-active role rather than just act as an additional pair of hands.

Over the years I found that most technicians were limited in their career by their lack of education rather than any lack of inherent ability. Over the years in Culham several of our young technicians went on to greater things when we encouraged them to work part time for a degree or higher qualifications.

The laser and the optical input system, with a large

helium neon alignment laser, was set up on Peter's vibration-proofed optical benches. To our relief the vibrations which you could feel through your shoes, in places severe enough to make your feet feel numb, were not transmitted to the critical optical components. No movement of the He-Ne beam could be detected. The first major technical obstacle had been overcome.

During this installation, Nicol Peacock, the team leader joined us. It took a while for the Russians to understand his rather abrasive style of humour, not to mention his strong Glaswegian accent. He was soon liasing with John Sheglov, his opposite number on the *Tokamak T3* team, familiarising himself with the spectroscopic properties of the *Tokamak* plasma. This was the area of his real expertise or his 'comfort zone' in modern parlance.

A difficult exercise was the alignment of the laser beam through all the optical system. Our plan was to use reflections of the He-Ne beam to simulate the plasma scattering volume, but this idea had to be abandoned due to jamming of the target mechanism under vacuum. Instead, we filled the torus with nitrogen and depended on the scattering from that. We were forced to do this in the evenings for safety reasons when no one was around. The Russians were a bit sensitive about safety as they had just had a fatal accident a few weeks earlier when a physicist was electrocuted on the experiment. In fact there was a move to make us take safety examinations, until Nicol Peacock explained to them the ultra strict safety regime we were accustomed to back home in the U.K.A.E.A. which was much more restrictive than their rules. They backed off having decided not to force the issue.

Once we had synchronised our electronics with the

Tokamak plasmas we could fire the laser at any time required during the plasma shots. I hardly need to add that all the Russian plugs and sockets were totally different to the British varieties and that caused a few headaches. After the interfacing was accomplished it really was a collaborative experiment, we could monitor the plasma current and light on our own scopes in the screened room for the first time.

Tension began to build as we were now ready to try stray light shots, with no plasma present, to see if our collimator and laser dump worked to cut out the stray light. Initially the stray light was depressingly high, but after a few days realigning and a somewhat radical decision to dump the beam energy on the ceiling some fifty feet above us, we reduced the stray light down to an acceptable level. This was relief because Artsimovitch had started to get worried and pressed us fairly hard on what the problems were. Derek continually reassured him that he and I knew how to sort it out as we had done it all before back in England.

We were now ready to try laser and plasma together at the same time, firing the laser as the plasma reached its peak density and temperature. But, all we could see was the plasma light signal – no sign of the scattered laser light pulse. Nerves were now getting frayed and Artsimovitch was showing signs of impatience.

However he did not lose his sense of humour as I found out one day when I was working alone on our equipment. As he cast his very sharp eye around our equipment he suddenly asked: 'That long piece of black thread or cotton leading from the spectrometer to the screened room, what is it for?' I explained that it was part of Peter Wilcocks' special shutter, that it was fired with such force that it jammed and the thread had to be tugged to release it. Lev roared with laughter and said: 'That is what I call real physics,' and he walked away chuckling to himself.

Unfortunately it was now becoming obvious that the plasma was emitting more light than the levels the *T3* team had claimed when we had made our planning visit. This could be a major problem to us as it would swamp the small scattered laser light signals we anticipated.

Derek wanted to explain to Slava Strelkov, the Tokamak team leader, our thoughts. But before he could, Nicol went up to Artsimovitch and told him that the *T3* plasma was 'dirty'. This was technically correct, because the light that originates from the plasma is greatly enhanced by the presence of impurities. But Nicol had not chosen the most tactful way to express it as it lost any subtlety in translation from English into Russian. Lev Artsimovitch erupted and his words are best left to the imagination.

The problem, it turned out, was rather mundane – it was dirt, or rather dust, that had caused the trouble. The small sapphire window situated on the underside of the torus through which the light measurements were made was covered with dust. It was the attenuation of the plasma light that had given rise to an optimistically low level of light emitted from the *Tokamak* plasma.

Ironically history was to repeat itself some twenty years

later on the European *JET* experiment in Culham. This time, coatings on the light collection windows modified the spectrum of the scattered laser light resulting in false temperature measurements.

Tensions were building up between Derek and Nicol due to the mismatch in their personalities, but as neither of them is still with us, it would be inappropriate to dwell on this aspect and I don't think it impeded our progress in any way. I gained the impression that the Russians were rather amused by their disputes but they also seemed to enjoy a bit of cut and thrust in their scientific arguments.

We were in turmoil due to our basing our signal-to-noise calculations on over-optimistic background light and we had committed to the wrong type of laser.

This non q-switched version with its long pulse did not have the power for the scattered light signal to stand out above the background plasma light.

Chapter 12

During all this frenetic activity we had enjoyed visits to the Bolshoi Theatre. Like all cultural activities in Russia at that time, it was somewhat surprisingly organised by the local cell of the Communist Party in the Kurchatov. It seemed to be the one thing they were good at and our Russian colleagues saw nothing unusual in this.

It is an amazing experience to enter the Bolshoi for the first time. There is a visual explosion of crimson velvet, ornate gold carvings and crystal chandeliers, coupled with an excited buzz of conversation and the discordant sound of the large orchestra tuning up. We managed to see two ballets, Swan Lake and The Sleeping Beauty, and there was the added attraction of some very good and free champagne in the intervals. We had even been provided with tickets for an opera in the Kremlin Theatre. This place seemed very familiar when we realised that this is where the top Soviet Politicians make their speeches. We must have seen this countless times on TV news bulletins.

We were also very fortunate to visit the Armoury in the Kremlin, where they housed the Russian equivalent of the Crown Jewels. At that time this was a privilege rarely granted except to Party VIPs and the Diplomatic Corps assigned to Moscow.

This was slightly marred by armed guards in very close

attendance. Any loitering was discouraged by a gun pressed to our backs. We even managed to see the over subscribed and brilliant Moscow State Circus, then in its beautiful 19th century headquarters.

I was lucky enough to experience some cross-country skiing with the *T3* scientists when the rest of the Culham team was away. The night before, there was a serious debate amongst some of the top Soviet scientists as to which wax should be used to coat the bottom of the very narrow wooden skis to suit the predicted snow conditions. They all turned up at the flat, used our gas stove to melt the wax and pass the skis over the gas flames to make sure they were well coated. As a result the fumes could be smelt for days throughout the flat

The routine was to catch a train out from the main Moscow station for a few stops and then ski across to another line for a return journey to make a large loop. This involved a bus journey to and from the Moscow train station amongst the locals with our ski equipment. I was surprised how accommodating and good-natured the Muscovites were because we had to stand at the bus entrance or exits which impeded those getting on or off. I could not imagine the average Englishman being so sanguine.

We had a few adventures that could have ended badly. One of the party spotted moose tracks and it appeared they had young with them, which can make the animals very aggressive. There was an instant panic in the ranks, even though we had lit a fire which I was assured would keep wild animals away from us. There is a photograph on the back cover that shows us in the woods with upended skis stuck in the snow

We made a rapid change of course, which had the effect of us getting totally lost, until we came across what was obviously a highly sensitive military area, with a triple barb wire security fence. Alarmed, one of the Russians whispered to me: 'For Gods sake don't talk. If the guards hear English we could be in trouble.' One of the women in our group went up to a heavily armed guard and explained we were lost and could they point us towards the railway line for Moscow. The young soldier, suitably charmed, gave her the correct bearings and we were on our way again.

One of the stronger men then challenged another to a climbing race up some fir trees – with their skis on. A bit like the Canadian lumberjacks do with their traditional climbing irons. They managed to get up to about fifteen feet before one clattered to the ground when a branch collapsed, which broke about two feet off the end of his ski.

All this was greeted with a lot of laughter before we moved on with myself feeling somewhat inadequate. Very shortly, I was to have this confirmed in a somewhat painful manner.

We were making good progress until we came to a steep downward sloping ice-covered hill which would have challenged even the most skilled of skiers. Jura Brobrobski, a really strong individual, realized I was in trouble as a novice. Before I had time to hesitate, he said: 'Hold on to me and we will go down together'. I clung on and we managed to get half way down before our skis became entangled and we somersaulted to the bottom of the hill to the amusement of the others. I did not break any bones but I ached for days afterwards from the bruises. I don't know if it was true, but I heard a few years later that they showed a video or film of my tumble in *T3* parties for some time after our stay in the Kurchatov.

On another occasion, I was in the laboratory on my own when the *T3 Tokamak* was being conditioned or 'cleaned' as the Russians put it. The liner of the machine was baked to a high temperature as the plasma was pulsed repetitively at a high rate, so no experiments were possible. An administrator came running in and said another group from the laboratory was going on a day trip to a couple of towns of historic interest. There was a spare place if I wanted to go. I jumped at the chance because otherwise I was not in for a very interesting day.

Socially it was a bit embarrassing for me, because I soon realised this group worked on a highly classified project and they felt uncomfortable talking to me as they did not know how I fitted in the Kurchatov Institute. So I just tagged along and kept to myself.

The highlight of the day was a visit to Vladimir, which was famous for its monastery and the church of the Saviour and St. Euthimius. This had been beautifully restored and we spent a few hours wandering around and taking in the architecture and the various religious artefacts that included some very important icons, painted in superb detail. I noticed that my companions were very ill at ease inside the church, something I had previously perceived when we had visited churches in Moscow with other Russian friends. In fact some were even reluctant to enter a church, I suppose because they were conditioned under the Communist regime to be, at the very least, agnostic.

After a really enjoyable day, the coach returned to Moscow in the dark. It was quite a long journey so they stopped for a comfort break in a densely wooded area. I was a bit puzzled when somebody shouted to me: 'You can't go in the woods by yourself, somebody must go with you'. A large man accompanied me amidst a lot of ribald laughter and comments that my Russian was not up to translating. As I climbed back into the coach one of the women, who spoke good English, explained to me that the problem was the bears, which will attack people on their own but will rarely trouble two or more people. Apparently they are quite a problem in the outskirts of the city where they empty the rubbish bins in search of food and have been known to attack house owners who go out to investigate the noise.

We also managed to see an international soccer match, Russia versus Northern Ireland. George Best was supposed to have played, which resulted in a huge crowd of disappointed Russians when he did not turn up. I think the only British there besides us were some of the diplomatic corps from the Embassy. It was a freezing cold evening and a very uninspiring match in which the players were just going through the motions. The Russians won 2-1.

Perhaps one of the most iconic experiences as far as I was concerned was when Derek and Marion wanted to visit a famous Russian poet's dacha outside Moscow. The same Jura

Brobrobski, who had gone to my aid when skiing, claimed to know how to find it and after a short rail journey we stepped out several miles into snowy open country. We managed to get ourselves totally lost and we never did find the dacha. Then suddenly on this beautifully sunny Palm Sunday morning we saw a gaggle of old and bowed Russian peasants, all dressed in black, streaming out of a little church, clutching willow twigs or palm crosses. That must have been the same scene that had been enacted for hundreds of years without change. They did not even look in our direction. We did not exist in their world.

In contrast, the young technicians liked to tell us about their summer camps with the Young Pioneers or Young Communists. Their photographs made our 18-to-25 holidays look like a Sunday School outing. This prompted them to bring out photographs of the *T3* team's holiday when they were flown out to the Siberian Lakes by seaplane. There were shots of some of our distinguished colleagues disporting themselves in the style reflected by naturist magazines. I was beginning to think I had led a sheltered life.

We noticed that the whole *T3 Tokamak* team seemed to socialize with each other as a group rather than with outside friends. I suspect this was for historical reasons from when they all worked on classified military projects in the Kurchatov and could not talk easily to those outside the fence. To the best of my knowledge this does not happen in the United Kingdom, almost the reverse in fact.

We were surprised how few of even the senior scientists had travelled outside the Soviet bloc, but as they said, they had plenty of scope for travel within their own confines and, as far as we could determine, this was all paid for.

They all seemed to be dismissive about the attractions of other Iron Curtain countries. We suspected it was because the Russians were not too popular in their client states.

I think the rest of our team and I were all a bit disappointed at how apolitical they all genuinely appeared to be. We were to a man, used to having a good political argument and Peter Wilcock was actually a Tory councillor back at home in Wantage. But here in Moscow there seemed little appetite for even a debate in this city, where the bookshops were full of dramatic posters showing Soviet workers in revolutionary mode, striking militant poses. The revolutionary mood had apparently petered out. Perhaps we were experiencing the start of the decline in the influence of the old Communist order.

Chapter 13

In 1968 the U.K.A.E.A. and the government were still smarting from the activities of the recently convicted Soviet spy and theoretical physicist Claus Fuchs. He had been carrying out his dual role, cosily ensconced in Hangar 8. This was adjacent to Hangar 7, where *ZETA* and most of the Fusion research work was located. As a result, any U.K.A.E.A. staff travelling to the Soviet bloc were subjected to rigorous security briefings before a visit was allowed to proceed.

We did not think the KGB would pose any problems as long as we did nothing silly. We felt safe, enjoying the powerful patronage of Lev Artsimovitch and we knew the prestige that scientists enjoyed in Russia was immense. However we were to find that the KGB activities were not a figment of the imagination, even in our privileged position.

Soon after we arrived Derek and Marion Robinson pointed to at least one advantage of being 'bugged'. One breakfast time they had commented out loud that a bulb had burnt out in the kitchen and debated who to ask for a replacement. When Marion returned from her routine morning shopping she found the bulb had been replaced. They had also noticed that visiting Russians were very formal in their conversations in the guest flat but relaxed back in their own apartments.

Nicol Peacock had a very nonchalant attitude to the KGB threat until, one evening when we returned to the flat, after a hard day in the lab, there was a shout from Nicol's bedroom. He then rushed out brandishing his brief case. 'Its locked! Its locked!' he shouted. It transpired that it contained his personal documents and because he couldn't lock it, he kept it inside a locked suitcase. Nicol, generally a pretty phlegmatic character, was visibly shaken. When he mentioned it to our Russian colleagues the next day no one seemed surprised. One said: 'It's when you don't know who the *they* are interested in, it is time to worry'.

On the lighter side, one day a party of VIPs and their minders were walking past the experimental area and were confronted by a security door with a secret security numerical touch-pad that barred their progress. Derek calmly walked up to them and in fluent Russian told them the security code. In blissful ignorance the party thanked him profusely. We never knew how Derek came to learn this sensitive bit of information.

My only real brush with a KGB operative was when I was visiting the Berioska shop on my own one Saturday morning. A young smartly dressed Russian came up to me in a friendly fashion and asked in a good English accent if I was English. I nodded and he asked if he could talk to me to practice his English as he had just graduated as an interpreter.

That could only mean one thing to me, that he was a KGB operative so I was immediately on my guard. He asked me what I was doing in Moscow and was I enjoying the experience. When I told him I was a guest of the State Committee working at the Kurchatov Institute, his jaw dropped. He was obviously on a fishing trip and the script had not prepared him for that scenario. After a few niceties, he made his excuses to go but before departing he asked what I thought of his English. 'Technically, very good, but stilted. In fact a bit old-fashioned,' I told him and suggested he listened to BBC Radio Scotland. I was not joking. A linguist at GCHQ had once told me it was the accepted standard on pronunciation. I think the poor chap walked away feeling he had made the wrong career choice.

The only other vaguely sinister happening was when, alone, I visited the impressive Tretiakov Art Gallery on a Sunday morning. It appeared to be devoid of other visitors except for an attractive teenage girl who always seemed to be interested in the same art sections of this huge building as me. She avoided eye contact and I kept a good distance from her. Could have been nothing, but in those days it made one aware of one's vulnerability in that situation.

On the matter of spies, coffee is the great tongue liberator, seemingly more effective than alcohol. This is what I have found when I have had the opportunity to speak informally to several very senior weapons scientists on both sides of what was the Iron Curtain. To a man they all seemed very dismissive of spies saying they had never received any input from such sources. In any case they would be so worried about planted misinformation or systematic disinformation that they 'would not trust the messenger' anyway. I found this was a bit like finding out the truth about Father Christmas, spoiling my romantic notions about spies.

I often wonder how many unfortunate people who are lured into spying, end up in prison, are tortured and even executed - all for nothing. Nobody would trust their information anyway.

Perhaps the last word on this intriguing topic goes to that infamous intelligence officer, Peter Wright, who caused H.M. Government so much embarrassment when he published his memoirs describing his activities. Though I never worked with him, I met him a few times in GCHQ in Cheltenham when he was waiting to meet my division head – either as a friend or professionally, I never ascertained. The few occasions he walked through our open plan office a respectful silence descended. Whenever I asked about him I always received a reproving look and no reply. Over a coffee and a *Penguin* chocolate biscuit in the distinctly unglamorous canteen one day, not in a Pall Mall gentleman's club as favoured in fictional spy stories, he suddenly said: 'I don't know how you fit in to this business young man, but the main thing to bear in mind is that the Cabinet Office is much more interested in what our friends in the West are up to and think, rather than the Reds. Those are the real secrets of diplomacy'.

Chapter 14

It was now into the month of June and we had to revert to plan 'B' to overcome the higher-than-predicted plasma light levels. We switched to Peter's 'belt and braces' 'q' switch kit which we had pre-packed back in Culham and had been rushed out to Moscow. Peter modified the photomultiplier amplifiers to handle the new fast signals. We now had a laser with a thousand-fold increase in output power in a 30 nanosecond-wide laser pulse. It was left to Derek and Volodiya to install the Pockell's cell (the fast optical switch) into the laser while Nicol, Peter and I were back in England for a break.

When we returned to Moscow we found that this much more powerful laser was to generate a new set of problems. After a few shots we discovered that no laser light was reaching the plasma. Disturbingly we found this was due to bubbling in the quartz prism that directed the output beam from the laser amplifier to pass vertically through the torus. After weeks of detailed investigations, we found it was caused by our system being too well aligned. Reflected light from the various surfaces was doubling up the beam intensity (or worse) as it returned through the prism, exceeding the damage threshold for the quartz. We managed to cure this by deliberately offsetting the optical components in the laser path.

One of these damaged prisms sits on a window sill in my house, a dramatic reminder of what can go wrong in physics experiments.

Optical physicists recognise that one of the most difficult exercises in the laboratory is the absolute photometric calibration of the detection systems that measure the amount of scattered light we collect. We wanted to be able to relate the scattered signals to the plasma density. For this we used a standard calibrated ribbon tungsten lamp from The National Physical Laboratory, Teddington, which gives out a known number of photons, or calibrated amount of light.

We then had a genuine scientific difference of opinion between members of our team. Derek and Nicol favoured using the direct radiant method, where the filament is viewed directly but with an attenuator in the light path, while I argued for the method that David Evans and I had trusted over many years, namely the alternative irradiance technique where the light from the lamp is reflected in a true Lambertian fashion from an aptly named Russian opal flat.

We each obtained widely varying results with large errors and after seriously doubting each others' competence, it was reluctantly agreed to go with 'my' method. Not surprisingly this well-proven method gave us much more consistent results and we adopted this method of calibration for the remainder of our experiments.

We had run out of some of the most critical components – the quartz prisms – due to laser damage, so our ever-reliable Bill Ball back in Windsor worked around the clock to make replacements. The Diplomatic Bag came in useful to get the finished items to us quickly: the British Embassy proved very helpful and of course were very aware of our collaboration with the Kurchatov.

This helpfulness had been reinforced by the Culham team being invited to the Embassy, when the then Labour Minister for Science and Technology, Wedgwood Benn, (Tony Benn) visited Moscow for some high level discussions.

Later, Peter and I were the only ones able to accept the invitation to the Queen's Birthday celebration at the Embassy. We were welcomed by the British Ambassador and his wife and a long line of British Diplomats. It was a splendid occasion on an extremely hot day in the Embassy Gardens, with all the Military Attachés in whites and it seemed every foreign ambassador in Moscow present. It was a somewhat surrealistic experience, the excellent Champagne cooling in what must have been Victorian Zinc Hip Baths, and the splendidly-robed Patriarch of the Russian Church, standing alone, as were two Chinese Diplomats, in splendid isolation. Nobody seemed to want to talk to them, but they seemed to enjoy the refreshments and the champagne.

It was a long walk back to the nearest metro and after taking on board so much liquid refreshment, I was very uncomfortable by the time we had crossed the Moscow River bridge and reached the walls of the Kremlin. I spotted some sheets of corrugated iron leaning against the Kutafa Tower and quickly dived behind them for a very welcome relief. Peter and I laughed as we walked on, speculating if this was an offence in Russian Law – showing disrespect to State property.

Chapter 15

Derek and Volodiya pushed on with the experiment in early July while the rest of us returned to the UK for a break.

They were faced with a crop of technical problems with the laser and stray light but after a brilliant concerted effort and several late nights they succeeded in optimising the scattering system.

Then dramatically there came the breakthrough. On July 22nd, Derek excitedly telephoned Culham to say they had observed clear scattered signals, above the background plasma light. What is more, they were seeing signals in several channels away from the central laser channel. These were the first signs of a broadened scattering signal, marking progress which was the long awaited breakthrough. In fact, Derek's very cryptic work sheet in the yellowing laboratory notebook (Figure 6) probably represents one of the most understated accounts of a major scientific breakthrough. Just a simple: *'Indicates Te = 1 K eV'*

This was the moment that confirmed the Soviet Fusion claims for plasma electron temperatures of 10,000,000 degrees Celsius. In fact this was probably the highest temperature recorded in the history of mankind, up to that time.

The historic *Polaroid* photographs showed the raw data with the sharp laser scattered light spikes standing clear of the background plasma light, totally unambiguous evidence of

Thomson scattering, just like David Evans, Alan DeSilva and myself had first observed in laboratory plasmas back in our Oxfordshire laboratory some five years earlier.

Nicol returned to Moscow almost immediately, but Peter and I had to delay our return because of pressing family matters. In my case my father had suddenly died of lung cancer, which was a severe shock because my sister and I were not aware how advanced the disease was. This naturally took a lot of the shine off our success as far as I was concerned.

By the 6th August some 88 plasma shots had yielded scattering results that indicated electron temperatures of up to 10,000,000 degrees Celsius and densities higher by 50% than those previously measured by microwave techniques by the Russians themselves. These key parameters were measured at various plasma radii using our scanning optics. In other words, it confirmed all the Russian claims and vindicated their confidence in the *Tokamak* concept, earning them just reward for decades of hard work.

Back in Culham the Director, Bas Pease, hearing the good news, telephoned Harold Furth, the Fusion Director, at Princeton University, U.S.A. He had been eagerly waiting for the call and the senior management at Princeton immediately made a major policy change to switch from *Stellerators* to *Tokamaks*.

Also, somewhat unusually, the editor of the influential science journal *Nature* was waiting for the call. He was keen to have a scientific breakthrough to publish in their centenary edition. So they 'held the press' until a paper with the *T3* scattering results reached them.

Before that, Derek was to make the first public announcement at the end of September of our results in a keynote post-deadline talk at the International plasma physics conference in Dubna, U.S.S.R..

It was at that time we were called out of our screened room during an experimental run. This was for a photo-shoot for what was the Russian equivalent of the old *Picture Post* magazine. We were somewhat startled when a very attractive Russian girl in a white lab coat was placed between us. We assumed it was to make the science look a bit more glamorous. Nobody in the *T3* team knew who she was.

We then stepped up the physics program to extract the maximum benefit from what was now a routinely functioning Thomson Scattering Diagnostic. For the physicists, this included firming up the Beta (poloidal), a good measure of plasma performance and the scattering derived plasma energy with electrical measurements of plasma diamagnetism.

Bas Pease had flown in to celebrate the success of the collaboration, for the preparation of the *Nature* paper and add his authoritative stamp of approval to make the deadline for the November 1st gold-covered centenary edition.

Then Nicol Peacock gave the eagerly-awaited invited paper presenting our results to the American Physical Society Plasma Physics Conference in Los Angeles, which was very well received. Many years later, when he was very ill, he told me that was the proudest moment of his scientific career.

The British team's last experimental run on the *T3* was in December, in high temperature neutron-producing conditions with electron temperatures up to 15,000,000 degrees Celsius.

Derek and Marion Robinson returned to the UK in November, exhausted after their thirteen-month tour of duty was completed.

Our chief technician, Harry Jones, then flew out to bring back the equipment that the Russians did not want to retain. They had agreed to pay the full commercial rate for a large part of the apparatus, but we could get the very sensitive secret photomultipliers back, without causing a diplomatic row with the Americans.

All our formal physics results were published in *Her Majesty's Stationary Officer Report R.107*, which serves as a standard reference on *Tokamak* physics. To this day, battered and well thumbed copies of this iconic report can seen lying around in fusion labs around the world.

Chapter 16

Back in the UK we could hardly believe that our work in Moscow had been such a total success, nor the impact it was to have on fusion research.

Our unprecedented collaboration between Culham Laboratories and the Kurchatov Institute in Moscow provided another giant leap for mankind, this time for East-West relations.

The story even prompted a question in the House of Lords, recorded in *Hansard*: a learned Peer, congratulating the British team on their success in Moscow enquired: 'How did the British team of scientists measure temperatures of 10.000,000 degrees Celsius?' He received the imaginative reply: 'I suppose they used a very long thermometer'.

Our success was recognised by the Royal Society when they invited us to the annual Queen Mother's soirée in Carlton House Terrace, London, to mount an exhibition to describe our work in Moscow. This very prestigious event is designed to showcase the best in British scientific research to the Fellows of the Royal Society, the scientific establishment, politicians, industrialists, the City and the press. This was a very formal occasion, where the dress code was evening dress with decorations and orders to be worn. We responded by having an animated model made of the scattering experiment, which included some of the original laser components such as a Ruby amplifier and helical flashtubes. But the pièce de resistance was the simulation of the laser beams, plasma light and the scattered light by rotating polarisers and coloured optical plastic sheets. The effect was dramatic and a very good representation of how the experiment functioned. In fact, it looked a lot more interesting than the actual experiment.

The U.K.A.E.A. management footed the bill for this exhibit, which we suspected cost more than the actual experiment, but the end effect was so impressive and drew such favourable comment that we felt it was money well spent. We took it in turns to man the display and talk to the distinguished visitors. I was particularly fortunate to have the pleasure and honour of meeting two very famous sons of very famous fathers, namely Sir George Thomson and Sir Laurence Bragg, two of the most distinguished names in British science. Here I was talking to Sir George, an early pioneer of nuclear fusion research, and what is more, his father had discovered the electron. They both smiled at me kindly as I hesitated, somewhat overawed by the experience, looking for words to describe the physics of Thomson scattering and the problems we had to overcome in Moscow. The irony of the situation certainly was not lost on them and they were keen to go through every detail of our experiment, especially some of the laser technology. They must have been with me for half an hour and as they bad me farewell, Sir George turned and said: 'My Dad would have been very impressed by what the Culham team have achieved'. That was a moment for any physicist to savour.

I had hardly recovered my composure when Sir Richard Huxley FRS, the eminent biologist, came up and introduced himself as Bas Pease's brother in law and asked if he was around. I told him that he was due later and he then proceeded to question me in great detail on the physics, explaining that he was very interested because Bas had talked to him a lot about our venture to Moscow. Men of his calibre are such complete scientists and have a deep understanding across the board with the ability to understand the basic principles of just about any scientific topic.

All in all it was a very impressive evening. Our public relations people said the feedback they received about our contribution had been very positive. I was surprised to learn from one of the Royal Society Fellows that the Queen Mother really enjoyed these occasions and had a genuine interest in science, which stemmed from the war years when she saw how much of our success in winning the war was due to British scientific prowess.

The New Scientist featured a profile of Nicol Peacock's group which covered the Moscow experiment and the wide portfolio of other pioneering spectroscopic topics.

The success of our scattering work in Moscow proved to be a watershed in world fusion research. From then on, throughout the world, the emphasis in magnetic confinement was firmly based on the successful Russian *Tokamak* concept.

Chapter 17

The successful outcome of the Moscow adventure was to lead to many positive repercussions that would considerably extend my horizons both in physics and geographically.

Almost immediately I was invited to the Swedish Centre for Fusion Research at the Royal Institute of Technology in Stockholm. This was in a consultancy role to advise on a suitable Laser Scattering diagnostic for their plasma device, a reversed field pinch. They had an expert optical physicist in Dr. Bertil Wilner and an ex-pat peripatetic laser specialist, John Tonks, so they were quite capable of building and exploiting their own equipment. Anyway I spent a few days in this interesting capital city in a snow-less December, which was a pity because there were flood lit ski runs through the sloping Institute grounds. I think that they felt relatively isolated in Sweden so they were keen to encourage guest lecturers. My hosts were keen for me to give a talk on the potential of Scattering techniques beyond the measurements we made in Moscow. They certainly wanted their 'pound of flesh'; I was told it was normal to give a two hour talk. I must admit this was beyond my normal range and I was not really prepared for that. However the feedback I received afterwards indicated they had been generally impressed by what laser diagnostic techniques could do for their program, and how powerful a diagnostic tool laser scattering could be.

Stockholm was certainly an expensive place and I was surprised when taken out for dinner with a senior academic who had spent several years in Culham. He said the salaries were not good in the Institute, and the professional classes really get hurt by heavy taxation. He said his family could rarely afford to eat out and wryly added: 'the best thing to be in Sweden is to be unemployed and shack up with an unmarried mother, you get the best of both worlds'!

Chapter 18

One of the first indications that international collaboration was stimulated, as a result of our Moscow experiment, was the setting up of the European mobility agreement that would allow scientists from member countries to work freely in other Fusion laboratories. My first involvement in this new scheme was to carry out a laser scattering experiment on the Frascati Plasma Focus experiment in the C.N.N.E. Laboratory outside Rome.

The *Plasma Focus* device is as different to a *Tokamak* as you can get. It was invented independently by our old friend Fillipov in the Kurchatov and Mather in the United States: for unabashed military motives. It is designed to produce X-Rays and neutrons in copious quantities.

Culham had adopted the compact Mather design. Physically it is very simple, just a 5 cm diameter solid conductor surrounded by a co-axial cylinder, 10cm diameter and about 25cm long, in low pressure hydrogen or deuterium. 40,000 volts was switched with spark gaps across one end of the cylinders and the resulting plasma drives itself along until pinching itself, producing a very dense plasma ten million times the density of a *Tokamak* plasma. But significantly it produces neutrons at the same rate as a nuclear weapon in a few tens of nanoseconds. In Culham, Nicol Peacock's group had built a

Focus basically as a diagnostic test-bed. Peter Wilcock, ad been so important in the technical side of the Moscow equ... ment, designed the fast high voltage switches .

Nicol was very interested in the spectroscopic riches the plasma would yield, while my interests were two fold: to measure the parameters of this dynamic plasma; and in the process advance laser scattering techniques. In some ways this was an academic exercise which involved some very creative Ph.D. students, whose studies added greatly to the understanding of this dynamic plasma.

A major breakthrough was the first experimental demonstration of the existence of filaments in plasmas when we measured the change of the angle of polarisation of a Ruby Laser beam as it passed through the plasma. David Muir developed a sensitive method to measure the very small angles involved. This vindicated the work of the avuncular and highly respected Professor Malcolm Haines of Imperial College, London whose theoretical studies had predicted filamental behaviour in plasmas for many years.

At the same time we developed some very sophisticated laser diagnostics that could be applied to Fusion physics in general. We were able to take advantage of advances in detector technology, which greatly increased the amount of data we could collect.

We enjoyed considerable financial support from the Unites States Air Force without carrying out any military research for them. All they required were three-monthly reports on any experiments we carried out. Three U.S.A.F. colonels insisted on travelling to Culham to monitor the contact which always ended up in the *Barley Mow* pub, popular with visitors to the laboratory in those days. One of them also had the interesting job of evaluating all 'flying saucer' reports in the U.S.A. But he remained unconvinced that they existed, mainly on the grounds of the surveillance capabilities of the U.S. military which would detect any intruders. It used to take all of our scientific imagination to provide a report with any serious content every three months, but despite that I think they had very good value for their money.

Although the work we did had no military connotations, it seems Israeli Intelligence had other ideas about our motives. We had two visitors purporting to come from an Israeli laboratory and claiming to be plasma physicists.

It turned out to be one way traffic. Suspiciously they subjected us to a severe inquisition but were very evasive when we tried to find out which establishment they came from. We never did find out who they really were, but the odds were that they were from the scientific arm of the *Mossad* who had become curious about the reasons for our American funding.

The Frascati trip was like the Russian exercise again: two of us made a planning trip to prepare for the experiment. This time Phil Morgan was with me, he had worked in Frascati before, and with me on the Culham Plasma Focus for several years. He was an expert on Laser Interferometry and had pioneered holographic techniques that yielded brilliant visual as well as physics results. The son of a Welsh farmer he spoke fluent Welsh and rapidly picked up any foreign language. He always kept us entertained at the lunch (or any meal) table with an endless stream of jokes. Many of these were of the most basic farmyard nature, the meanings of which were lost on our international friends. In fact I used to tease our continental friends that 'they could not claim to understand English until they grasped Phil's jokes'.

It is hard to imagine a more glamorous site for a Research Laboratory. Frascati is nestled in vineyards in the Alban Hills above Rome. The town itself is a beautiful medieval place full of elegant and charismatic eating places. My favourite was the Bella Vista situated on a terrace that overlooked the plain of Rome. The locals jostled for places on the long trestle tables, drinking the local wine from large carafes to accompany huge plates of olives and bread on sultry summer evenings.

Charles Maissonier was our host as the Group Leader of the very large, but in the event, not very successful *Plasma Focus*. This was based on the Fillipov design which used much larger electrodes than the Mather version. Charles was one of the elite French scientists educated at the École Normale and was destined to be the Head of Euratom. A very sophisticated, well turned out individual, I once had occasion to comment how smart his jeans were: 'Oh, my tailor made them for me!' He never tired of reminding us of the superiority of the French education system, especially in mathematics.

I was to return for the actual experiment some months later. I drove to Rome on my own, stopping overnight in a small family hotel on the French side of Mount Blanc Tunnel and then called in at the University of Milan en route. I arrived in Rome exhausted and resolved never to make such a journey alone again because I had felt incredibly lonely and vulnerable, to my surprise considering I was pretty well travelled.

When I arrived in the laboratory there were some glum faces. Apparently there was a custom officers' strike and our equipment, on a special Euratom lorry, could not cross the border between France and Italy. We could only suppose it was physically blocked by hundreds of other lorries, as it had Diplomatic status and normally would have been waved through customs. As a result I had to hang around, so I 'piggy backed' on some other experiments to justify my being there.

My host in the laboratory was Massimo Gallanti, a young Italian physicist, who had worked for his Ph.D. in Culham in our diagnostic group. He had married into a highly placed Italian family and his mother-in-law gave lavish parties to the Roman glitterati, literary elite and government ministers in their Ostia beach holiday home. This was not Massimo's scene so he asked me to go along a couple of times for moral support, but I found all the Italian guests charming and friendly and they seemed genuinely interested in what Nuclear Fusion was all about, so much so, that I felt quite relaxed in this social mileau which was far different to the circles I usually moved in back in England.

My knack of meeting famous people was rewarded in a somewhat curious manner. My hostess, obviously highly embarrassed, pointed out to me a foppish Englishman, standing in a corner in splendid isolation. 'Mike,' she said, 'will you look after him? He is Anthony Burgess, a famous English author, you will know his most notorious book *A Clockwork Orange*'. A Rome newspaper editor I was talking to, said to me in a stage whisper: 'arrogant bastard, none of us here want to know him'.

Actually, hitherto I had been impressed by Burgess's work, so I was able to walk up to him and say: 'I am the other token Englishman here and I enjoyed your book *English made Plain*' He looked startled and said: 'you sound bloody Welsh to me, what are you doing in Rome?' I explained I was a Plasma Physicist. 'Oh!' he said, 'Out of curiosity I read a couple of books on the subject so I could master the topic.' The Italian newspaper editor had described him well. It was a short conversation as he soon subsided into an alcoholic stupor and I slipped away to find some more pleasant company. It was sad to have one's illusions of such a famous author shattered so profoundly.

After a few weeks my wife and three children flew out to join me for our summer holiday. We had the use of a large rambling stone house belonging Claude and Helen Rabour in Grottaferrata, a village higher up the mountain, where many rich Romans retired to escape the hot Rome summers. It was a fairly ramshackle place but full of character: vines and olive trees competed for space on the terraced garden. The Rabours had returned to Scotland for a holiday. The summer evenings darkened quite early and the fireflies darted about us when we dined al fresco on the patio, as we warded off the feral cats who tried to steal our food.

Before my family joined me Claude and I were alone together for a week in the house as his wife had returned to

England ahead of him. Here was man with his own set of 'devils' mainly due to him having fought with the French Foreign Legion in Indo-China. He had been involved in the flame throwing of the tunnels from which the Viet-Cong used to mount their attacks. He could never eat steak after that because it smelled of burnt human flesh. Also he had been forced to man isolated observation posts on his own, for months at a time in tropical conditions; this had taken its toll .

My worldly experience was notched up a few points when every day we drank coffee in a local tavern under the trees on a cobbled square. We were often joined by locals who seemed very different to the Italians I knew in the laboratory, but they all were friendly and always greeted Claude effusively. Then one day, almost casually, Claude turned to me and said: 'you realise that my Italian friends are the local *Mafia*, don't you? Eenrico keeps the records of houses that are burgled to make sure it does not happen more than three times, otherwise they would not be insured. The big chap with a cigar is the one you buy your stolen furniture back from.' He went on, listing all their activities in matter of fact terms and then reassuringly added: 'it is part of their code not to harm foreigners, in fact when your family is here and if you need any help, any of those you have met will swing into action!'

The Alban hills were full of interesting places to explore: Tuscolo, the birthplace of Roman civilisation; Castel Gandolfo, the Pope's Palace; and Lake Lago Albano, the deeply sinister black volcanic lake of indeterminate depth, all capped by Rocca di Papa, the hill top village. It was only a short train journey into Rome's impressive central station and we covered all the tourist essentials very efficiently so I had chance to explore the City before my family had joined me. Our children, ranging from eight to fourteen years old, enjoyed every minute: they said it was like being on a film set. The only thing that they did not appreciate was the Italians continually patting their heads; all three were very blonde!

Then of course we made several trips to the seaside: the closest beach resort happened to be Anzio. It was an emotional moment when setting foot on it for the first time, to think of the thousands of British troops who had died there. My present neighbour in Abingdon, now in his eighties, carried the *Union Jack* ashore there as a young soldier in World War Two. The same, now tattered, flag was to fly proudly above our local millennium street party in Abingdon some fifty-six years later.

Chapter 19

When I was told my duties in Culham were to be extended to take in commercial activities I thought that this would be a boring option, but I was to be pleasantly surprised. Hugh Bodin, my Group Leader, and an enthusiastic convert to the commercialisation of the U.K.A.E.A., had two avenues he thought would be fruitful for me to pursue. This was heavily conditioned by two destinations he loved to visit, Japan and Egypt. He took the esteem he was always accorded in Japan as a great personal compliment and always returned from a visit brimming with self-confidence. Nicol Peacock, a man of the world ,wryly commented to me in his best Glaswegian: 'its only because he is bledy old'.

Buoyed by a recent trip, he thought we should mount a charm offensive to obtain orders for advanced diagnostic equipment. As a result Chris Bishop, a promising young theoretician, was to accompany me to demonstrate the depth of Culham's intellectual force. He was carrying out pioneering work on the application of neural networks to plasma physics.

This is the complex process the human brain uses to handle the vast amount of data it has to accommodate. After an outstanding academic career he now heads up Microsoft in the U.K. and this potential was immediately recognised by our Japanese hosts who hung on to every word in his lectures.

For some of the time we went on our own different ways. Chris went off to give lectures to more specialised audiences in theory or mathematics in university and laboratory departments. I targeted the main Fusion laboratories where I was always well received. This was due largely to me being a personal friend of Professor K. Muraoka of Kyushu University who had worked closely with us in Culham for many years and was an enthusiastic anglophile . He was a very influential player in Japanese Plasma Physics and as a result I always found myself sipping green tea with the Director of each research institute through their very 'old boy' network. Wherever I visited, my hosts had done their homework and knew about my major publications and my status in the Culham hierarchy. Every time I visited their large facilities, such as *JT 60,* it was obvious that Japanese large industry was heavily involved. Beautifully engineered, the devices carried conspicuous labels, such as *Hitachi,* and these heavily involved firms saw Fusion as an important long-term investment. Despite all this good will I soon realised they did not need any help on Advanced Plasma Diagnostics, but even so, they made very polite promises to consider what Culham had to offer.

Anyway, Chris and I enjoyed the extensive hospitality and the initiation into various Japanese customs and were happily drunk enough to eat delicate slices taken from live fish in what was regarded as Japan's most charismatic fish restaurant. The chefs shouted, banged the cooking utensils, juggled with razor sharp knives and threw fish around like jugglers in a circus act. The attractive serving ladies, extremely buxom for the Japanese, somewhat overwhelmed Chris Bishop and myself with their blatant flirting as they leaned across the bar to serve us, fingering our ties and shirts. It was obviously a place for a night out with the lads and the all-male Japanese clientele surrounding us were highly amused by this behaviour. It was patently the 'done thing' to enter into the spirit of such proceedings so Chris and I, in relaxed mode, did exactly that.

It was a case of criss-crossing Japan on the high speed *Shinkansen* trains or internal flights to cover a large number of Fusion-orientated Institutes and Laboratories. From Tokyo to Nagoya and down to Kyoto and Kyushu Universities in the south. I had an embarrassing linguistic adventure when buying a ticket for the overhead mono-rail train that ran from Tokyo to an internal airport. Travelling alone, I was about to put my money into what I took to be a ticket vending machine when a smiling Japanese gentleman tapped me on the shoulder and said in perfect English: 'Excuse me sir, but do you really want to buy a tin of soup?!!' We both enjoyed a good laugh over that.

This very extensive and expensive exercise produced no immediate commercial advantages to Culham. But I am certain Chris Bishop's lectures were a good advertisement for Culham and provided a boost to its theoretical prestige.

Chapter 20

Much to my surprise, Hugh Bodin's interest in Egypt paid off through a friend of his, Professor Abdel Azziz of the University of Cairo. This leading academic had been invited to Libya to set up a Plasma Physics Department in Colonel Gaddafi's pet project, *The El FatahUniversity*, in Tripoli. Prof. Abdel Azziz had taken some key academic staff with him and had been given a substantial budget to set up a 'state of the art facility'.

After initial talks in Culham, it was clear that the Libyans wanted a complete plasma experiment, one that produced an interesting plasma for research, and at the same time was easy to run and maintain. It was mutually agreed that a *Thetatron* pinch device as pioneered in A.W.R.E., Aldermaston, with Culham-designed Laser Scattering Diagnostics, would satisfy these criteria.

During our extensive discussions it became apparent to me that Abdel Azziz was over tired or not well, so I suggested he should join my wife and I for a meal in our home with Bodin and his wife, rather than dine out as was planned in his itinerary. For some reason or other he seemed extraordinarily grateful for this gesture, even his wife was to mention this when I met her several months later in Libya. It turned out he was sickening with some kind of bug and our family doctor kindly turned out to treat him in his hotel room which was much appreciated and it was, fortunately, successful.

At that stage we could not cost the project without a visit to Libya, so I was joined by Peter Barnes, a very experienced Culham electrical engineer. He was used to designing and building Fusion devices and carrying out the associated project management. We had to have our passports translated into Arabic and special visas for our mission. We stayed at a well-appointed, hotel situated in the Diplomatic Quarter of Tripoli. It was well up to international standards and it soon became apparent that anybody doing business with the Libyan government stayed there. The barman made up for the lack of alcoholic beverages by blending the best chilled fruit juices I have ever tasted. After being exposed to Libyan summer temperatures I think even the most hardened alcoholic would have recognised them as an acceptable substitute. The only hint of anything sinister was the attention of a very well dressed Libyan gentleman who descended on us every time we entered the hotel lobby and appeared over interested in what we were doing in Tripoli. We declined his offers of hospitality saying we had a full social program with our El Fatah University friends.

A young Egyptian lecturer, Dr. Fawsy Menshawy, was our contact, in fact he was to be the prime mover on the project and very competent he proved to be. He had collected us at the airport after we had passed through the passport control with no problems, no doubt due to our powerful accreditation. Once outside the airport, the heat and dust blowing in from the Libyan desert hit us and I could not help contrasting this with the freezing conditions I encountered on my first visit to Moscow. At the end of the very straight road into the city there was a severe traffic hump, or *sleeping policeman*, to slow traffic down before reaching the built up area. Our driver took a great delight in telling us that it was quite common in the dark for drivers to bite off their tongue when hitting this obstacle.

Tripoli was like a large garden surrounded by olive trees, palms, vineyards and orange groves. The university was situated only a mile or so out of the city centre in what was essentially the start of the desert. We were somewhat startled by the fact that the entrance was manned by heavily armed soldiers, but they took no interest in us, then or whenever we were to come to and go from the campus. We learned later that they were stationed there to deal with any anti-Gaddafi factions or demonstrations. Students can always be relied on to form a protest movement, but here we gathered they were soon silenced.

The university was well appointed with very modern two storey buildings designed for the Libyan climate, spaced out on what was a well planned campus. The flat roofs had huge overhangs to shade the vertically slotted windows and the main entrances. Slots the full height of the building allowed the free flow of air through the halls and corridors. The plasma physics department had been allocated plenty of space for experiments and was well endowed with lecture theatres and practical laboratories. The experimental hall for the planned *Thetatron* experiment was very spacious, with electrics and all the services required for a large experimental assembly. It was immediately apparent that money was no problem here.

On arrival, we met the Dean of the Physics Faculty: a Libyan Professor of slightly more serious character than Abdel Azziz, but friendly none the less, greeted us: 'Welcome to our University gentlemen, we are very honoured that you Culham experts have agreed to help us, we hope you enjoy your time here and manage to visit some historic sites'. Then he went on: 'you can be sure of every help you need, any problems you can knock on my door any time, we enjoy the personal support of the President. It turned out that the Dean moved in the highest circles in the Libyan establishment and was one of Gaddafi's enlightened appointments. Despite Gaddafi's eccentric reputation it appeared that any decision he made that would benefit Libya or an individual citizen was usually very positive and rational. Also Gadaffi often took to a retreat in the desert surrounded by Bedouin Arabs and held open court for his people. Amazingly, to me anyway, it transpired that any Libyan subject who thought he had a good idea could approach his President, and if he could convince him that it was feasible, he would receive very generous State backing.

We could not help noticing that on the campus the students almost all adopted the standard western student garb of jeans and t-shirts, though we realised in later visits that a lot of the female students travelled to the university in traditional dress and then changed their attire! Somewhat strange for such an establishment with such radical roots.

Many of the girls were very attractive by any standards

and vivacious with it. Our Egyptian colleagues warned us in no uncertain terms not to get too friendly with these students as it could lead to a knife in the back from the girl's brother or relatives.

We were allocated a dedicated Palestinian technician who had a good physics degree from a English university but could not get a lecturer's post in Libya. According to him it was for convoluted Arab political reasons, but Peter and I put it down to straight discrimination. The poor old Chad gardeners also appeared to be treated as an under class. I was mildly reprimanded by a Libyan colleague one day when I tried to speak to one who regularly tended the gardens around the Physics Department.

We dined out in a very up-market roadside restaurant between the university and the city with the Dean, Prof Azziz and some senior University officials, all very friendly and relaxed. They were very puzzled as to why the U.K.A.E.A. had gone into a commercial mode. To their amusement we said we shared their bewilderment. They were all patently anglophiles and took great delight in telling us that: 'Gaddafi's pilot is British, his chief financial advisor is British', and they reeled out a roll of honour. To this day I am puzzled what flipped him into the international terrorist mode that has caused such international distress.

One of the most rewarding experiences there was to go into the souks in the evening after dark. Goldsmiths, silk merchants, carpet weavers, and vendors of just about any commodity you could think of, vied for our attention. Their shouts cascading through their range of languages; Arabic, French, and in desperation finally English. A heady scent of herbs, Arab cigarettes and cooking enveloped the whole place. What added to the pleasure was that I always felt totally safe there, even on the occasions when I was alone. Mark you, I always carried very little money and certainly not my passport and had only the cheapest of watches on my wrist. The University staff were astonished that I should wander about on my own, in fact they were quite concerned. I explained it was only an extension of the 'mad dogs and Englishmen' syndrome and I was pretty streetwise anyway and it was not exactly 'Laurence of Arabia' territory. We found that all the Libyan people we met were friendly and very courteous and of course there were never any drunks

There was a stark social contrast between the Egyptians and Libyans when we were invited to their homes. The Egyptians, with the exception of Abdel Azziz, were all married to Liverpool girls who they had met when in the University there, who were delighted to meet some Englishmen and have a good gossip. It was difficult for them to walk around in Tripoli without their husbands without being accosted, albeit usually in a good-natured manner. While in the Libyan homes the wives only appeared to serve us with refreshments and did not enter the conversations at all; it was a macho experience.

Our Palestinian friend and Fawsy Menshawy were obviously very competent physicists and knew what they wanted, so together with Peter and myself we soon managed to get an outline plan for the project together. Prof. Azziz was impressed with the proposal and even without knowing the cost told us to go ahead with supplying the whole package. He shook hands with Peter and me and said: 'You British and us Arabs enjoy the same code of honour, it is now a binding contract between both sides'.

We returned to Culham with a lucrative £2,000,000 order with no paperwork. The Chief Finance Officer turned pale when I told him we were going ahead on the strength of a handshake. He was singularly unimpressed by the 'code of honour' concept and was only partly mollified by the Director, Bas Pease, reassuring him: 'It's OK Ken, it really does stick if these chaps shake hands on a deal'. In the event the Libyan Embassy soon sent a very formal contract in Arabic and English, open ended for further work or effort.

The whole project was a much easier experience for me than the Moscow experiment. Most of the work was to fall on Peter Barnes and his engineering team as the *Thetatron* and its power supplies formed the bulk of the contract, while I only had to organise a straight-forward Laser Scattering diagnostic to measure the plasma temperatures and densities. This required no development work, just some logistics.

The next trip I made to Tripoli was in high summer. Peter and his technicians had already been out there a fortnight and stayed on the campus so they could get finished quickly. Peter showed me their excellent progress and some wild life that had joined in the experiment. He picked up a cable duct cover and there were bright orange cockroaches, about four inches long, nesting there. Apparently harmless, they served to eat the

other smaller insects. Peter and his team were pret
so Prof. Azziz laid on a full day's trip the archaeol
Leptis Magna, overlooking the sea. On a glorious ;
had the place to ourselves and the lizards, to enjoy
regarded as the best preserved Roman remains in the
Mediterranean.

Even in the laboratory we were continually reminded
that this was a Muslim country. Everything stopped when the
call for prayers sounded over loudspeakers on the campus.
Uncannily, the locals got out their prayer mats and kneeled
towards Mecca. While instructing the Libyan staff on how to
operate the ruby laser, the scattering equipment and other
diagnostics I became quite friendly with a Palestinian. We
enjoyed discussing politics and one day he said: 'The last thing
all the Arab Countries want is a Palestinian State as in a few
decades it would establish its intellectual authority over the
whole area'.

Prof. Azziz was delighted when all the equipment was
up and running and he could see his staff were well able to run
it for physics experiments. He even ordered another tranche of
equipment to extend his research facilities. The Libyan students
we came across all seemed very hard working and obviously
keen to take advantage of the superb facilities the University
offered.

Later I spent several days in Tripoli on my own to
discuss academic points with the research and teaching staff.
This time I was in the very well appointed *Beach Hotel* fairly
close to the University, usually used for international

nferences. But I found myself sharing the place with just a married couple who seemed intent on not making eye, or in fact any contact with me. One day after breakfast the very attractive wife left on her own came up to me and said in excellent English: 'I hope you don't think we mean to be unfriendly but my husband is senior officer in the German army and we cannot talk freely here, except to our hosts, for political reasons'. I made light of it, instantly realizing she meant the East German army: 'I understand your situation, I'm a British physicist setting up experiments for Gaddafi's El Fatah University and for good measure I have worked in Moscow as well'. She looked a bit startled at that revelation, but relieved at the same time. I only spoke to her once again after that when we were a respectable distance apart on the beach, both enjoying a swim. Some local Arab women were running in and out of the sea clad in full length white local dress, which not only had become transparent but clung to their bodies in the most revealing way. The German wife walked past me on the way back to the hotel and smiled: 'Those Arab girls might as well have been naked it would have been more respectable', and she was gone before I could reply.

There was a Tunisian waiter in the hotel restaurant, who was always keen to engage me in conversation in which we met linguistically half way, in English and in French. He quietly told me that his ambition was to open a Tunisian restaurant in London where he had relatives. The one night I was not receiving Libyan hospitality he asked: 'Will you do me the honour of joining me and my wife in our quarters for our sons second birthday party and my wife will cook you a special Tunisian meal'. His charming wife spoke quite good English and was very keen to know everything about my wife and children. She was an excellent cook and I supposed this would be their main asset for their London aspirations. I can still remember the main dish of lamb, apricots and almonds in a blend of herbs I could not identify. The olive skinned little boy accepted me easily and I was able to play the same games with him that I had with my own two boys at that age. I suspect the couple had led a very isolated life in Tripoli and were not encouraged to integrate with the Libyan community.

I was not going to escape the Tripoli episode without some fallout. Prof Azziz asked if I would give a talk on my work to the Physics Department, with the emphasis on Laser Scattering diagnostics. I had an evening to prepare a quick talk based on slides I always carried with me on my travels. The next morning he came running up: 'The Vice-Chancellor is on campus and he would like you to broaden the talk out to explain about Nuclear Fusion, he is a classical scholar with no formal physics knowledge'. I found myself facing all the top University staff from all the various faculties, but managed to explain things in layman's terms. Judging by the number and nature of the questions that followed they had been very interested. My encounters with English T.V. presenters and journalists had not been in vain!

Back in Culham I was summoned to the Directors office, I assumed for a debriefing. Bas Pease said: 'The Foreign Office have been raising hell because you gave a talk on Nuclear matters in a sensitive country without the proper clearance'. Before I could explain he went on: 'Luckily Dennis Wilson (the laboratory Secretary) was in Cambridge with the chap on the Arab desk and he managed to placate him'. Technically of course I was in the wrong but no damage was done.

I sensed a beautiful irony when later I was told that the Russians had built the Libyans a *Tokamak* device in an unidentified site a few miles away from the University, but we never found out any more information about the project. We suspected it was the Russians trying to diplomatically match our prestigious project, which we gathered, had impressed Gaddafi when he paid a visit after Peter Barnes and I had returned to the U.K.

Chapter 21

Culham went on to build its own *Tokamaks* after our Russian adventure. Derek Robinson launched his career by building a 'table top' version to study basic *Tokamak* physics. This was followed by a larger device, called *DITE*, more or less the same size as the machine we had worked on in Moscow. The now widely accepted Russian argument that was that the plasma properties are better in all respects if the impurity levels are kept very low. *DITE* was built with this in mind. Ingenious magnetic coils diverted the contaminated plasma into a chamber where the impurities were dumped on to a cooled plate.

Paddy Carolan and myself had been planning for a year a very sophisticated experiment utilising laser light scattering to determine the electric current profile in the plasma. Knowledge of this is paramount in the understanding of the stability and containment of the plasma. Explanations of this technique are beyond the scope of this book. Prof. Ian Hutchinson of M.I.T. in the United States in his standard textbook on plasma physics diagnostics, states: 'It it is impossible to overstate the difficulties in applying this technique.'

Operating right on the edge of electro-optical technology at that time, we obtained the first detailed profile of the electric current in a *Tokamak*. Paddy was in Germany at this time so it fell to me to show the experimental results to the

Director, Bas Pease, who was thrilled to bits at this physics 'first'. "Mike, go and show this to Roy Bickerton (the deputy Director) he will be impressed especially as you have measured a 'q' value less than one – pretty contentious stuff". This is a value of the twist in the magnetic fields in the *Tokamak* that contain the plasma.

I did not relish the prospect of this encounter because Roy thought spectroscopists, and Nicol Peacock in particular, were slightly mad. As I was Nicol's right-hand man he tended to think this had rubbed off on me, so he greeted me with a tolerant smile. It did not start well: 'You are trying to tell me this set of blobs is a meaningful measurement of plasma current and a *q* less than 1'! Holding the precious *Polaroid* picture which admittedly looked a bit like the night sky he looked very sceptical and he grilled me for an hour until I managed to convince him it was a meaningful result. He was one of the nicest of men but one of the most challenging physicists in Fusion research to discuss your physics ideas with. As I left his office he grinned and said: 'That is pretty good stuff that you and Paddy have produced, well done'.

These results warranted publication in the journal *Nature* and impressed the Americans sufficiently to ask me to give an invited talk to the Plasma Physics Division in Princeton University, U.S.A..

Colleagues had warned me this was like going into the 'lion's den' because of the intellectual high ground Princeton scientists justifiably occupied. But I think this normally very critical audience were somewhat stunned by the complexity of the experiment and were very generous in their praise. This had followed the first presentation of our results in the bi-annual Conference on the *Diagnostics of High Temperature Plasmas* in Santa Fe U.S.A.. These very specialised conferences provided a shop window for all the latest plasma diagnostic techniques and they were always the conference of choice for me.

One interesting feature was that the delegates were in two camps, one specializing in the diagnostics for laser produced plasmas and the other for magnetically confined plasmas such as *Tokamaks*.

Chapter 22

In 1978, the European Fusion Community decided the way forward was to co-operate on a large *Tokamak*. This was to lead to the highly successful European *JET* Project being built in Culham after much political procrastination, with the first plasma shots in 1986. It boasted impressive parameters, with a major radius of 2.96 metres, a minor vertical radius of 1.68 metres and a plasma current of 7 million amperes. In addition 68 megawatts of additional heating could be brought to bear if required.

The highlight was when it demonstrated the feasibility of nuclear fusion. Operating in a mixture of deuterium and tritium, the plasma acted as a reactor and for two seconds the fusion power peaked at 16 Megawatts.

Ironically, I was not to be involved in the laser scattering experiments on *JET* because Culham management wanted to retain key staff to maintain a viable U.K.A.E.A fusion physics program in Culham. I was to lead the key team on advanced plasma diagnostics with commercial targets as well as supplying diagnostics to *JET*.

To handle this portfolio, I was sent on senior management training courses in Cambridge and London, run by some of the most prestigious names such as Ashridge. Bizarrely, I found myself locked in syndicate battles with various heavyweights, varying from the Chief Brewer of Guinness to the Director for Research of the Royal Zoological Society. A very attractive red-head who was the Head Bio-Chemist for Schweppes added to this exotic mix of scientific managers.

But no training could match the experience I had gained in my involvement with the Moscow *Tokamak T-3* experiment in the late 1960s.

JET called on Culham spectroscopic expertise to carry out impurity studies on the plasma. We had known since the early Russian *Tokamak* work that impurity control was critical to the performance of the machine. So I had come full circle and was a spectroscopist again, albeit part time. My colleagues Patrick Carolan, Mike Stamp and Phil Morgan were the lead physicists and together we made major contributions, with European colleagues such as Professor Manfred Von Hellerman and Professor Kurt Behringer, to the understanding of the effect of impurities on *JET* physics.

I even found myself in charge of a small team which went to the University of Dusseldorf,where they had a small *Tokamak* with a beryllium wall. The purpose of the exercise was to establish a reference set of spectroscopic data should *JET* or other large *Tokamaks* utilise beryllium as a wall material in the future.

The success of *JET* and other large *Tokamaks* in the world was to lead to much bigger things. Who could have imagined that some of the most diverse nations in the world would put aside their political and cultural differences and pool their resources to build the biggest *Tokamak* to date in e, France, to take the penultimate step to producing a usion reactor. This device, *ITER*, is scheduled to be ial in 2026. To achieve fusion reactor conditions plasma currents of 15,000,000 amps contained in a torus 6.2 metres radius and a plasma 2 metres in radius are required.

I found myself after retirement in a consultancy role to the Nuclear Fusion programme in one of the more esoteric topics. I had became involved in 'detritiation'. One potential problem with *ITER* is that the plasma-facing walls, if made of graphite, could become coated with a hydrocarbon layer containing absorbed tritium. It is important to remove this film before it cracks and falls to the bottom of the torus as an undesirable tritiated dust.

Glenn Counsell, Kieran Gibson (University of York) and myself came up with the idea of 'photon' cleaning and to use *JET* as a test facility. This used an elliptical reflector to focus the light from a powerful fast pulsed laser flashtube onto an existing wall tile in *JET* which had been exposed to a tritiated plasma over a long period. The water-cooled cleaning head was mounted on the *JET* remote handling arm and scanned across a test area. Technically the experiment was a great success and post mortem analysis showed that the irradiated area was virtually free of tritium.

We did have one water leak into the torus which did not go down well with the vacuum group. I was subjected to some barbed jokes about us using wet photons!

Chapter 23

We survivors of the team who travelled to Moscow in the late 1960s with our ruby laser, to confirm the outstanding Soviet research claims, feel more than a tinge of pride in our achievements. After all we had helped to make *Tokamaks* recognised as the way forward in magnetically confined fusion research.

It is somewhat salutary to think that you have achieved what is generally perceived as one's most important, or rather, the most newsworthy work by the time you are 35 years old. Yet it is a harsh fact of life that the scattering experiment in Moscow was so important to the world nuclear fusion programme, that anything that my colleagues and I were to do subsequently, would pale into insignificance by comparison. I know now how authors feel when they are remembered for one particular book they have written rather than for an extensive portfolio of superior work.

In fact, since those exciting times in Moscow I have carried out much more demanding and advanced scattering experiments, pushing this ultimate plasma diagnostic technique to much higher levels. Even in retirement I have been able to contribute by advising the new and young generation of 'scatterers', most strikingly, Dr. Mike Walsh, who masterminded the Culham *MAST* Tokamak Scattering System, which is the most sophisticated in the world. Implemented by Martin Dunstan, a veteran of many scattering experiments, this installation utilises a ruby laser and eight YAG lasers to probe the *MAST* plasma.

Drawing on my experience, I was able to incorporate optical design features we had pioneered in the 1960s and evolved over the years. This coupled with some new ideas proved to be critical to the success of the equipment.

This remarkable diagnostic produces 56,000 temperature and density measurements in one plasma shot. A far cry from our laborious single point measurements we struggled to make in the old days.

Of course these advances are only made possible by huge improvements in the efficiency of detectors, optical materials and ever more sophisticated optical design software. The latest data acquisition techniques greatly add to the information obtained during one plasma shot.

There is one certainty in the future of Nuclear Fusion. That is that every reactor will depend for its optimisation and operation on a multitude of probing laser beams.

Future generations of scientists will scatter laser light from electrons just as my colleagues and I first did in the 1960s, to provide one of the great investigative tools of Nuclear Fusion science.

Our Russian colleague's view of the British team. Cartoon used in a U.K. lecture by Academician Boris Kodomtsev. He was later to become Director of the Kurchatov Institute.

Figure 1: **The author working on the hand-built laser in 1964 for the first definitive laboratory measurements of plasma electron and ion temperatures. The discarded and dangerous Kerr Cell optical switch is in the foreground on the right hand side . The plasma device is behind the dexion frame on the left of the picture.**

Figure 2: Mike Forrest, last to board the Pakistan Airlines Boeing 707, Moscow-bound with 5 tons of experimental equipment.

Figure 3: **The British team – Harry Jones, Nicol Peacock, Mike Forrest, Derek Robinson and Peter Wilcock**

Figure 4: The Culham Scattering Equipment coupled to the
T3 Tokamak on the right.

Figure 5: The massive concrete anti-vibration optical laser support benches in the basement area under the *T3 Tokamak.*

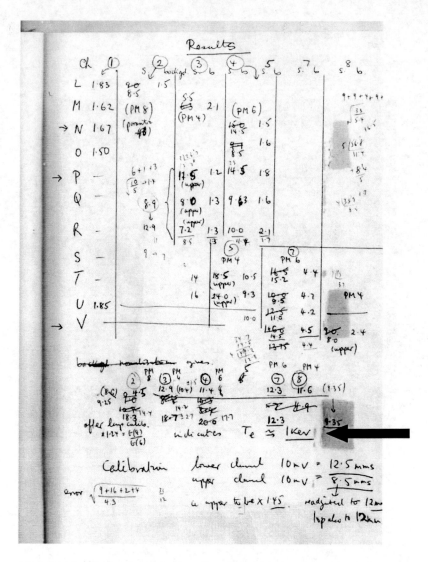

Figure 6: First Results. Derek Robinson's cryptic comment (arrowed): 'indicates Te ~ 1 KeV. or 10,000,000 degrees Celsius'!

147

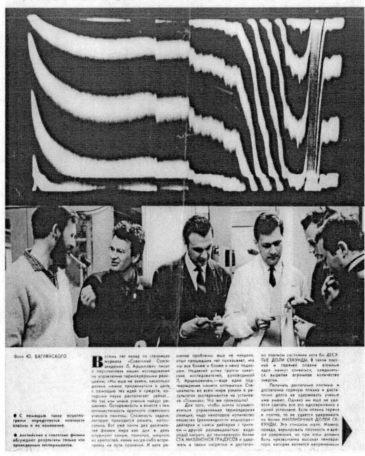

Figure 7: Russian popular press coverage of the Anglo-Soviet collaboration. Left to right: Nicol Peacock, Volodiya Sannikov, Peter Wilcock, Mike Forrest, Derek Robinson and S. Mirnov.

FORREST

A doughty lad from Gwent there came,
Diligence was his nature and FORREST his name;

In all things his life is ordered most precise,
In women, drink and gambling he is without vice;

From early morn to dusk his day is set by juices gastronomic,
The precision of his body-clock is really quite "phenomic"! ;

At ten precisely by the clock, matters scientific fled his heid,
As coffee, biscuits and jolly company were all his need;

At noon his "inner man" drove him to the canteen,
to be the first in the queue for chips and pie and icecream;

Punctuality is the very nature of the man,
Verily, he is as regular as All Bran;

Enough about his character and now about his chores,
If lasers were his speciality then optics held the core;

Well could he set up apparatus and his help was often sought,
In Tokamaks and Pinches his expertise he wrought;

He was among the chosen few to see the scattered light,
And pee against the kremlin wall when his bladder felt too tight;

[A not uncommon situation when working overseas,
But Moscow in particular has a dearth of WC's;]

At Culham by Oxenford his hands he never sat on,
He helped to measure q of (r) and fluoresced the atom;

Until today we find him here........QA'd and Cost-Accounted,
A shadow of his former self, a horse that's been sorely mounted;

The knacker's yard would seem his fate,
but I tell you this with feeling;

When at last he passes through the gate,
He will turn as frisky as a yearling.

NJP 18/08/92

Rough humour: **Nicol Peacock's tribute to the author on his retirement, after a poem by Robert Burns.**